PRAISE FOR DICK A.

"Cancer hurls a family's life into a storm and gives cause to remember that what we enjoy today is all we know for sure. And that adversity can bring out the best. This is a powerful story about one woman's climb . . . even higher than Everest!"
—Peter Hillary, mountaineer, speaker, and expedition leader, and son of Sir Edmund and Lady Louise Hillary

"An incredible book. I was taken on an inspirational journey. The book shares how a life-changing, life-threatening event can give us courage to be real. In the story of Dick and Deb's journey, I saw fear conquered by love, anger conquered by patience, doubt conquered by hope, and weakness conquered by faith. I want to share this book with those I know and love who are battling their own journey."
—Frances D. Roberson, Executive Director, Community Hospice Foundation, Rocky Mount, North Carolina

"I found this book to be helpful, honest, and hopeful to persons who are going through their journey of cancer. Your willingness to be so transparent with your own emotional valleys that you both faced will serve to give permission to other couples in taking ownership of their own feelings, rather than continue to live in denial and feelings of guilt. This book will serve as a catharsis for those individuals who are cancer patients and those who are serving as their caregivers."
—Dr. Ross Bauscher, Evangelism Growth Team Kentucky Baptist Convention

"Honesty, faith and humor are woven throughout this candid book of a couple's journey through breast cancer. Every aspect of their personal and professional lives and experience with cancer is explored, compared and contrasted. Through it all, their love sustains them, their faith upholds them, and we are touched and blessed by what they reveal about their challenging journey."
—Barbara L Bouton MA, FT, hospice professional

"I was so moved by Dick and Debbie's life journey. *Don't Ever Look Down* should be mandatory reading for all couples dealing with cancer.

The love Dick and Debbie share and their willingness so openly tell their story is incredibly inspiring. They are a true testament to love conquering all; even the cancer mountain."

—Danielle Knox, show host, *The Balancing Act*

"*Don't Ever Look Down* is more than just a story; it is a guide to assist you in your own journey through the heartache of cancer. You will be touched by their honesty, hope, and yes, humor. It is an inspiring story of love and commitment that should be required reading."

—Teresa Young, breast cancer survivor

DON'T EVER LOOK DOWN

SURVIVING CANCER TOGETHER

Dick & Debbie Church
with
Diane Moody

JOURNEY PRESS

Charlotte, Tennessee 37036 USA

[handwritten inscription, left:] Janet Thank you so much for all you do for cancer survivors Blessings Dick

[handwritten inscription, right:] Janet Thank you for your great friendship! God bless you in every way. Debbie Church Jeremiah 29:11

Don't Ever Look Down: Surviving Cancer Together
Copyright © 2011 by Richard and Debbie Church, with Diane Moody.

Published by Journey Press, a division of Sheaf House Publishers, LLC. Requests for information should be addressed to:

Editorial Director
Sheaf House Publishers, LLC
3641 Hwy 47 N
Charlotte, TN 37036
jmshoup@sheafhouse.com
www.sheafhouse.com

Library of Congress Control Number: 2010938345

ISBN: 978-0-9824832-3-7 (softcover)

Unless otherwise indicated, all Scripture quotations are taken from the HOLY BIBLE, NEW INTERNATIONAL VERSION®. Copyright © 1973, 1978, 1984 Biblica. Used by permission of Zondervan. All rights reserved.

Scripture quotations marked (NASB) are taken from the NEW AMERICAN STAN-DARD BIBLE®. Copyright © 1960, 1962, 1968, 1971, 1973, 1977, 1995 by The Lockman Foundation. Used by permission.

Scripture quotations marked (NKJV) are taken from the New King James Version. Copyright © 1982 by Thomas Nelson, Inc. Used by permission. All rights reserved.

Scripture quotations marked (KJV) are taken from the King James Version of the Bible.

Cover design by Hannah Schmitt.

Front cover photograph by Dick Church.

Photo of Dick and Debbie Church by Bev Moser, Moments by Moser.

Interior design by John Boegel.

11 12 13 14 15 16 17 18 19 20—10 9 8 7 6 5 4 3 2 1

MANUFACTURED IN THE UNITED STATES OF AMERICA

CONTENTS

Dick

To Deb, my companion in life and undeniable hero.

Debbie

To my wonderful husband, who is my life, breath,
and heartbeat.

Introduction

DON'T EVER LOOK DOWN

—Dick

"Climbing is stupid! You're an idiot! Do you have a death wish?"

I've heard these statements from dozens of well-meaning people. My mom, my dad, sisters, and best friends have all "encouraged" me like this. It always fills me with such joy and confidence. But I know they are only concerned about my safety.

As I gather my gear and bounce to the door, I do feel rather stupid and idiotic. I wonder if I do have a death wish. Maybe there is something deeply and psychologically wrong with me. Did I have a horrible experience as a child that makes me want to die? Did I climb up the side of my crib and attempt to leap off into the abyss? Was I so depressed over being force-fed that jar of strained beets that I couldn't take it anymore?

As crimson slobber surely oozed out of my mouth, I can only imagine I must have screamed, "Good-bye, cruel world!" Though I'm sure it didn't sound like that. I could probably only utter, "Bye-bye!" Any other time, this fond farewell would have been cute. Evidently, I must have changed my mind and nestled back into my pink blanket with my thumb in my mouth because I'm still here.

Pink? Could that be the problem? By the way, I still like beets, but every time I eat them I slobber profusely and wear a pink shirt. As a result, I don't eat them in public.

One of my favorite questions others ask about climbing mountains is a simple one: "Why are you doing this?" I always pause for a few moments struggling for an answer. "For fun" doesn't cut it. "I don't know" sounds ridiculous. But then, I have a stroke of genius. I remember the most famous answer to a similar question asked of George Mallory: "Why do you want to climb Mt. Everest?" The English mountaineer who made three separate attempts to climb it said, "Because it's there." Many have questioned if Mallory really said that. Most likely, it is believed, a newspaper reporter invented that quote. But it sure sounds hardcore, doesn't it?

On his third expedition in June of 1924, Mallory and his climbing buddy Andrew Irvine both disappeared high on the North East Ridge in their attempt to be the first ones to summit the world's tallest mountain. The last time he was seen, he appeared as a mere "dot" to another climber at around 27,000 feet. His body was not found until seventy-five years later near the same ridge. There is no proof at all that he made it to the summit.

On many of my climbs I have wondered about falling on the way down. I came to realize that coming down is more important that going up. If you don't make it down, you can't brag about climbing it!

On 29 May, 1953, at the age of 33, Sir Edmund Hillary and Sherpa mountaineer Tenzing Norgay became the first climbers known to have reached the summit of Mt. Everest. *Time* magazine rightly defined Hillary as one of the of the most influential people of the twentieth century.

Falling is a horrible word when you're several hundred feet above the ground hanging precariously on a rock face. Many things go through your mind, but I guess the most important one is: *Am I going to die?*

In college, I was the president of the Outing Club. As a group of guys (and one or two girls), we did all kinds of adventurous things. We went caving, climbing, scuba diving, skydiving (I didn't do that), and hiking. (Occasionally I took one of the girls on an outing—meaning we went out for pizza, a treat reserved only for the president, thank you.)

One day we took John on a rock climb for his initiation into our club. If he made it to the top, he'd be in the club. If he didn't, he'd be in the club. (We were desperate for members. We needed the monthly dues.) Since he had never climbed before, we went over the nuts and bolts of the sport with him.

We had carefully planned his introduction. We arrived at the mountain and hiked up to the climbing area. We picked our normal rock face for the initiation ceremony. John walked up to it, looked up at it, and gasped. He first uttered a few words I've heard golfers say when they shank a shot into the woods, followed by a very logical question.

"Are you kidding me?"

"Oh, come on, John. You can do it!"

Seasoned members like me silently laugh whenever we bring new meat to see this rock face for the first time. We know all about the hundred-foot vertical face. It has beaten every one of us during our own initiation rites. Handholds are plentiful for about fifty feet; above it, a treacherous climb.

"It's a piece of cake! We've all climbed it," we lied.

I scurried up around the side of the face where it wasn't too steep. I carried the rope and fixed a top-rope belay around the usual tree, as top-roping is the safest way to climb.

In an effort to boost his confidence, I would always shout to the initiate below, "I think this tree will hold you."

I threaded the rope through a carabiner on a sling wrapped around the tree at the top and dropped both ends to the ground below. Then we helped John get ready. We gave him a harness and a climbing helmet. He wore decrepit old tennis shoes, totally unsuited for climbing.

"They'll be fine," I commented, standing there in my expensive, state-of-the-art climbing shoes.

On one end of the dangling rope, we tied a figure-eight knot and hooked the loop into a locking carabiner connected to his harness. The other end served as the belay—where another person basically holds onto one end of the rope to give the climber safety. As a climber climbs, the belayer reels in the rope, giving slack or tension as needed. But most important, if the climber falls, the belayer can stop him.

Belaying is critical. If you fall, it saves your life.

Most people have seen or heard about free-climbing, when a climber uses no rope or protection at all. Look on YouTube and search for "free-climbing." A lone climber may be a thousand feet up, and his feet and hands are his only protection. A slip will catapult him to his death. Now in my opinion, a free-climber is an idiot and stupid. (I wonder if he eats beets?)

Our initiate, John, was ready. We repeated the usual mantra: "On belay?"

"Belay on."

"Climbing?"

"Climb."

John started up. "Piece of cake!" he shouted.

At first, plentiful handholds and footholds the size of cars made for easy climbing. But a few minutes later, he stopped. He looked up.

"This is impossible! How in the world do you get to the top?"

"John, don't be a pansy. It's easy!" we answered, offering the same encouragement each of us had also heard and knew didn't work.

"You can make it!" his belayer shouted. "I've got you if you fall!" (I'm sure that translated *when* you fall to John.) "Keep climbing, and don't look down at the ground."

"Don't look down" doesn't mean you can't glance down from time to time to search for footholds, to see where you have placed your last piece of protective climbing hardware, or to get an idea of your location on the rock relative to the ground. But for inexperienced climbers, staring at the ground can become hypnotic and paralyzing.

John started to get what's called the "sewing-machine leg." Pure nerves and fear causes muscles to weaken, making the climber's legs shake up and down like a sewing machine needle. It's exhausting.

Down below, we all laughed. "Don't look down at the ground, John. Keep moving . . . you're looking good."

But he looked down. He kept looking down, too frightened to move. "Tension, tension, tension!" he cried over and over, until the belayer took all the slack out of the rope. John tried to move and slipped.

"Falling! Falling!" he yelled.

The belayer easily stopped his fall. John was fine but scared to death. He dangled there for what seemed like an hour. The belayer slowly began easing him down to the bottom.

As he neared the ground, he asked, "Can I try it one more time? I can do it. I know I can!"

We were shocked. Few initiates ever wanted a second try.

"Sure," we said, our silent laughter growing audible, making him even more determined.

John started up again following the same process.

"Don't look down," we reminded him. "Keep going. You're looking good!"

Finger-holds the size of pennies and footholds not much larger offered little help, but they moved him up inch by inch. Occasionally he stopped and started to look down at the ground, the sewing machine still plugged in.

"Don't look down!" we encouraged. "Keep going. You're looking good!"

Frankly, we were impressed and jealous. Deep down inside, we were hoping he wouldn't make it. If he did, it would make the rest of us look bad!

How he did it, I will never know. But there he was, standing on top of that steep rock face, waving at us with a big smile. From that day forward we called him the Fly.

After her double mastectomy Deb had two drainage tubes placed into her chest wall. At each end of the tubes a suction cup gathered the accumulated fluid. The cups would fill, and the contents had to be poured into a measuring cup and the amount recorded. The suction cups were then squeezed and attached back onto the tubes. A cloth wrap was tightly wound around her body, covering her chest. The cups dangled uncomfortably.

The first night home she was allowed to take a bath, but instructed to keep the cloth wrap on and not get it wet. After her bath, we had to measure the fluid. I have a hard time with medical stuff (more on that later), especially if there is blood involved. But this was no time for jokes or wincing. We unpinned the cups from the wrap and measured the contents. I tried not to cringe the first time I saw the contents, but it was so much more difficult for Deb.

I hugged her gently and told her everything would be okay. As I placed my arms around her and pulled her to me, it felt different than before. My chest was so much closer to hers. It was as if we were two pieces of a jigsaw puzzle, tightly connected to each other. No breasts separated us.

She cried. I tried to comfort her, telling her how our hearts were so much closer now, how it seemed like we were truly one flesh. When her heart ached, mine did too.

The second night, Deb was allowed to remove the cloth wrap before showering. We unpinned the suction cups, and I placed one in each of her hands. Slowly, I unwrapped the cloth until the final unveiling— the pain, the staples, the tubes, and the startling reality. Each one of these screamed at her, the absence of her breasts audible.

A horizontal red line, all that was left of a cherished femininity. Silence swallowed us. We tried to control our shock by ignoring it.

Neither of us looked down as I helped her into the shower. Afterward, as I patted her dry, we both averted our eyes. But the bathroom mirror didn't have to glance down. It stared at us, never blinking, like the play-by-play account in some strange movie. A mirror never lies. Deb saw the surreal image reflecting back at her.

This can't be me, she must have thought. *That's someone else . . .*

Debbie Church, the oncology counselor. Not the patient. She's the one who comforted other ladies in the mirror. But now, that strange woman in the mirror was her. And all her wise and caring counsel that had soothed so many others could not help her now.

Once a year I make my Christmas pilgrimage to Victoria's Secret. I love the smell and all those nice pictures on the wall. It seems like everything in the store is either red or black with white lace. For some strange reason, I always feel very awkward in that store, like I'm doing something wrong when I go in.

One Christmas I bought Deb a sexy outfit. While shopping for it, I was rummaging through the different outfits when a young college girl approached me. "May I help you?" she asked.

Immediately uncomfortable, I coughed, then mumbled, "No, thank you, I'm fine. Just browsing."

Just browsing? How weird is that? I felt like some pervert.

After I selected the garment (what there was of it), I joined the long line waiting to check out. Fifteen-year-old girls stood in front and behind me, all buying R-rated materials, at least from my perspective. But perhaps I'm too old school. Only one other man stood in line with me, with at least thirty people behind me.

Finally it was my turn. Naturally my ATM card wouldn't go through the first time the eighteen-year-old girl behind the counter swiped it. The line backed up even farther, and heads stuck out to stare with disgust at me like so many cars on a crowded interstate. Next time I'll use cash.

I knew what came next.

"Would you like a box?" she asked.

"Do you have an unmarked cardboard box?" I wanted to ask, but didn't. They never do.

Victoria's Secret needs to change the colors of their boxes and bags. Everyone in the mall recognizes those pink and white bags. I feel like a walking billboard, a sex commercial. It makes me feel like some sort of . . . addict. I wanted to hide it in my Belk bag, but I hadn't gone to Belk.

What if someone asks me what I have in the bag? I wondered. I suppose I could tell them Victoria's Secret has the best selection of thick floor-length flannel nightgowns in the mall.

I'm not sure why, but it's always such a relief to see another guy carrying one of those bags. I want to follow him. Like *I'm da man . . .* part of a secret male club. But then he hurries into Belk, and I'm left on my own, holding the bag.

Speaking of holding the bag, years ago when our son was just five years old, I gave Deb a sexy little teddy on Christmas Eve. The next day as she was putting the turkey in the oven, Scott came over and whispered in her ear, "Mommy, don't tell Dad, but I don't think he could afford the bottoms that went with your outfit." It's a favorite family story, as you can imagine, and ever since then I've made sure there were bottoms to go with any outfits.

A mastectomy is a horrible experience. In today's culture, a woman's desirability is depicted with unblemished bodies, sculptured figures, and bust size. Scantily clad women advertise everything from cars to chocolate. All they have to do is bend over and show some cleavage, and the products fly off the shelves. Sadly, many women define their sexuality by their weight and bra size. Sadder still, many men use these same criteria as a measuring rod to gain their attention. It's pathetic, really.

Deb is no different from other women. By this I mean she measures part of her beauty by how her body looks. She's tried all the diets and exercises, bought balls, pills, shots, videos, books, stair steppers, and dozens of other weight-loss apparatus that promise more than they deliver. Then to have part of her "sexual" anatomy quite literally whacked off is devastating.

Now, on her second night home, as she quickly wrapped the towel around her, I felt my heart breaking for her all over again. She picked out her favorite blue pajamas. I guess she wanted to feel normal again. I bought them for her several years ago when I didn't have the guts to go into Victoria's Secret. (I probably bought them at Belk.) I carefully helped her put them on, then turned down the covers on the bed for her.

It all felt so automated. It seemed as if we should do what we always do: I take the dogs out, Debbie reads, and I watch some television downstairs for a while. That was normal. That was real.

But normal had vanished.

Halfway to her side of the bed she stopped, put both hands over her face, and began to weep bitterly. She didn't move toward me for comfort as she had done so many times before. The grief and fear and pain paralyzed her. She felt scared and all alone.

I walked over to her and hugged her, but I felt alone too. It was as if both of us were lost in a great sea of uncertainty, unsure of our emotions and destination.

Deb looked down and buried her head into my chest. She clamped her arms tightly against her body and clenched her fists beneath her chin. She continued weeping, the sobs originating from the deepest recesses of her soul. She looked down at the ground and said the words that broke my heart.

"Don't look at me. I am so ugly. Please don't look at me."

I didn't know what to say or do. I am not a perfect husband. I have said and done so many stupid things over the years, wrong things at the wrong time. So I simply embraced her, then I began to weep too. I placed my hands under her chin and gently lifted her face toward me.

"Look at me!"

She tried to drop her face again. I pulled it back up.

"Look me in the eyes!"

She dropped her head again and buried her face into my chest, but I wouldn't let her.

"Look at me, Deb." I caressed her face in my hands as she closed her eyes. In our thirty years of marriage, I have never seen her so pitiful.

"Open your eyes and look at me, Deb."

She hesitated, then looked up. Tears streamed down her face and mine.

Then, as if God gave me the words to say at that very moment, I said, "You are the most beautiful person in the world. I didn't fall in love with your body. I fell in love with your heart, mind, spirit, and soul.

"Don't look down. Don't you *ever* look down again."

Chapter 1

THE COUNSELOR BECOMES THE PATIENT

—Deb

I punched the down button in the hospital elevator and quickly glanced at my watch. *Gosh, I'm going to be late for my 2 o'clock.* I'd met with "Susan" before, but she was extremely anxious about her treatment and the side effects it was having on her. As an oncology counselor, I had talked to hundreds of patients who had suffered from these same side effects. And even though my expertise was more in counseling, I certainly understood the sickness she was experiencing.

She also wanted to talk about her family and how her illness was affecting her eleven-year-old son and his grades. I wasn't a child psychologist by any stretch, but any type of cancer causes dramatic changes in family dynamics.

My beeper sounded again. *Susan must already be waiting at the office.* As the elevator continued its descent, I felt stressed, needing to be there for Susan, but knowing the last half hour had been equally as important. My other patient, Mr. Rhodes, had put up a valiant fight against prostate cancer, and it was obvious he would lose that fight within a few short hours. The family had gathered by his bedside. They had thanked me for helping them through such a difficult time.

I always felt so inadequate when such things were said to me because I never felt like I had done as much as I should have. But families seemed to recognize sincere empathy, and, if nothing else, that was one thing I could give them. I had told Mr. Rhodes' family I would check back with them this afternoon, and they assured me they would still be there.

As I stepped off the elevator, then quickly opened the door exiting the hospital, the steamy Marietta, Georgia, day assaulted me. The annoying blast of never-ending hospital construction pounded in my ears as I hurried down another pathway that wasn't there the day before.

This is taking too long! I rushed up the back stairway of the Cancer Center to enter through the back door of my office, trying to catch my breath before meeting my patient.

At last I opened my door and welcomed Susan into my office. We exchanged pleasantries as usual, but before she could even start talking to me, she began to cry. Not unusual for my patients. Cancer and crying seemed to go together far too well. I kept several boxes of tissues in my office and handed her one.

Finally she started talking about her last chemo and how awful it had made her feel. She'd almost cancelled our appointment but knew she needed to talk. She told me she would share her feelings with her family, but they just didn't seem to understand what she was really going through. They tried to be empathetic and understanding, but they still expected her to fulfill her role as mother, wife, and daughter, and she just couldn't do it all.

"Debbie, how do you tell your family and your boss and everyone around you that things have changed so much?" Her voice strained as she looked directly into my eyes. "I have cancer! I have breast cancer! And it's *so* hard. The chemo makes me so tired. I'm losing my hair. I cannot do the things I used to do!" She buried her face in her hands and began to sob.

"It's okay, Susan. It's okay," I said, quietly affirming her. It was important to let her cry, but even more important to let her feel what she was feeling. No one else had let her.

When her tears began to slow, I asked, "Susan, what do you want to tell them?"

She pounded her fist on the arm of my couch. "I want to tell them exactly how I feel!"

"Well, why don't you? What's stopping you?"

She paused a moment before answering. "I don't know. I guess I don't want things to change either. But the changes are coming so quickly, and it's like an ocean wave coming at me and I can't stop it."

"You feel out of control."

"Yes! And I used to get control by being the mother, the wife, the employee. But I can't do it anymore." A single tear tracked down her cheek.

At this point, she needed some proactive advice. "Let's start with what you would like to tell your husband." She took a deep sigh, obviously trying to articulate in her mind what she wanted to say. "Pretend he's sitting right there beside you," I continued, "and I am here to help guide you. What would you say to him?"

"I would tell him I'm tired. I can't do it all like I used to."

"Why is that so scary to verbalize to him? Would he be mad?"

"No."

"Would he rage or say, 'I'm not going to help you!' or 'I'm not going to cook dinner or clean'?"

"No."

I paused for a moment, then asked quietly, "Susan, do you feel like your husband loves you?"

"Oh yes, yes. I know he loves me very much."

"So what is the fear? Where is it coming from?"

She looked down at her hands. "Debbie, I think the fear is coming from me," she answered, her voice barely above a whisper. "Because I don't want to have cancer."

October 2008

I was in North Carolina, staying at my sister-in-law's house. Standing in the shower with the water dripping over me, I did my monthly breast self-exam automatically, moving my soapy fingers in a rounded motion, pressing lightly to feel for anything suspicious. I stopped suddenly.

I felt a lump in my left breast.

Fear gripped my stomach.

After eighteen years as an oncology counselor, I immediately diagnosed it. *It's one-and-a-half to two centimeters . . . it's tucking in my skin . . . all the signs of cancer.*

I stepped out of the tub and toweled off. I looked at myself in the mirror and pulled my arms up just like they tell you to do in the diagrams. What I had felt in the shower was a reality in the mirror.

I don't want to think about this right now. I have an interview today.

A second round of interviews, in fact. Landing a job here in Wilmington would help get us moved to Carolina Beach where we wanted to be near family and, of course, the beach. I was excited for the first time in months. The past year had been filled with so many bitter disappointments.

Earlier that year I had worked for a group of twenty-one oncology physicians. It was my dream job. Before joining them, I had worked with oncology patients for eleven years, first in graduate school, and then in both Florida and Atlanta. As director of support services, I had the opportunity to work with cancer patients, their families, and caregivers in the hospitals and offices. I would counsel the families and help to lead them down the Road of Cancer as they traveled through the maze of appointments and the changes in their lives and in the lives of their families.

I loved this work, and unlike so many other people, I loved going to work every day, where the challenges would differ but the dynamics would be the same. I could use my hope, my faith, my expertise, and my care for these individuals every day. I led support groups and "Lunch and Learns," where we taught the patients and their caregivers how to cope with their finances, their depression, and a wide variety of relevant topics.

One day in May as I was driving back from one of these lunch meetings, a woman pulled out in front of an oncoming ambulance, forcing the ambulance to broadside my car. The impact demolished my car, and I was rushed by another ambulance to the hospital. Thankfully nothing was broken. But I had severe bruises, and two weeks later I began to have excruciating neck problems. Of course that led to more X-rays, and eventually spinal injections were required to help the pain.

Then just two months later, while still under treatment for my injuries, I was laid off from my dream job. I had worked with these physicians for seven years, and I was absolutely devastated. Because of the economic downturn sweeping the nation, they could no longer afford to offer counseling and supportive services to their patients. I ached for my patients. Who would guide and encourage them through the intimidating and often terrifying darkness of cancer?

I went through a period of profound grief. This was a job I had loved for so long, and it was such a natural fit for me. But I had to bury my grief and sadness and start looking for a new job. And believe it or not, my first two job interviews were near Wilmington, North Carolina, where both Dick and I wanted to live. With new dreams on the horizon, I was just beginning to experience a genuine excitement for the first time . . . until I found the lump.

At first I was completely dumbfounded. I had no idea what to do. I mean, I understood what to do, but I didn't do it. I didn't tell anyone.

I kept it a secret. By keeping it a secret, I thought the secret would go away, even though I had worked in oncology for years. It was a lie, of course. But I kept the lie to myself. I'd been taught never to lie, so I kept it to myself.

With Thanksgiving just around the corner, I couldn't tell anyone. Not even my husband Dick. Our son, Scott, was coming from Texas for the holiday. Our whole family was gathering at Carolina Beach in just a few weeks for Thanksgiving, and I didn't want to be the center of attention. I didn't want to bother Thanksgiving. It's one of my favorite holidays, one I look forward to because of the love and tenderness and sharing.

We have a tradition of going around the table telling what we're most thankful for. Sometimes it's the only time all year we have an opportunity to tell each other how we really feel about them, and we take it very seriously. It's become such a strong tradition that our daughter, Mary, plans for weeks what she's going to say.

I just did not want to ruin Thanksgiving.

The days and weeks went on, and I did nothing about it—except that I would reach down and feel my lump every day. I tried to permit myself to feel it only once a day because I kept thinking it might go away. I was already menopausal, so that could explain why sometimes lumps would come and go. But the lump did not disappear.

I could not tell Dick. Not only was I sure he would freak about it; I also knew he would call his sisters in North Carolina. They would insist I go to the doctor, and that would be the end of all our Thanksgiving plans.

And so it was on the way home from Thanksgiving when I finally told Dick I had a lump in my breast.

"Well, you've always had those fibrocystic lumps," he said. "That's probably all it is."

"You're probably right. But I think I'll make an appointment to see the doctor when I get back."

"I'm leaving town on Monday," he reminded me. "I'll be gone most of the week."

"Oh, that's fine. I'll just go see my OBGYN."

The following Wednesday morning, as my OBGYN examined my breast, I could see the tension in his face. "How long have you felt this lump?" he asked.

"About three or four weeks."

He looked at me. "Three or four *weeks*? How long has it been re-tracted?"

I swallowed. "About the same amount of time."

He covered me with the paper gown and helped me sit back up. "I'm going to send you to see a surgeon this afternoon."

At that moment, I knew.

I have cancer.

As soon as I got in my car, I called Dick and told him the news. "They want me to see a surgeon this afternoon."

"Deb, I'll be on the next flight home." I heard the tremor in his voice. "Don't worry, okay? I'll be home as soon as I can."

I called two friends and asked them to go with me. Just two short hours after seeing my OBGYN, I was lying on the surgeon's examination table, completely exposed. She looked at me in an attempt to be very comforting, but said, "We need to have a biopsy." As she looked into my eyes, I could read her body language. It was a scary, surreal moment for me.

I have breast cancer.

And I knew she knew that I knew. But then, I had known for over a month that I had breast cancer.

The biopsy was scheduled for the following week.

That night, I sat alone at home. I hadn't eaten all day, but I wasn't hungry. I was so anxious. My mind just kept swirling. The realizations kept coming at me.

How would I tell my children? How would I tell my relatives?

I needed my mom and dad so much, but they had both died in 2005. I needed their support, their encouragement, and their sympathy in that moment. I wanted Daddy to hold his little girl and tell me everything would be all right. And that's what brought the first tears to my eyes. I'd held them in all day, very stoic.

At 10 p.m. Dick walked in the front door. We literally fell into each other's arms and held each other for a long, long time. We let the tears fall, holding nothing back.

"You only thought it was a lump," he whispered finally. "Why didn't you tell me all you knew?"

"I thought if I didn't tell anyone about it, it wouldn't be real," I cried. "I'm as bad as one of my patients. It's called denial."

But Dick was angry. I wasn't sure if he was angry at me or about the possibility that I might have cancer.

"How can this be happening?" he bellowed. "You go for all your tests! You have all your mammograms! You do all the right things. How can this be happening to you?"

Over the course of the next few days while we waited for the biopsy, I sat in my favorite chair in our den, constantly chewing on my finger-nails, something I never did. But I was extremely anxious. I made Dick call the kids and tell them what was happening. He called his sisters and gave them the news as well. I called my older sister, Joan. I was surprised how everyone in my family thought it would all turn out fine. Over and over, they told us, "Don't worry about it!"

The reality of my experience, however, whispered loudly in my ear. Through the years, I had studied the lumps on breast models to know which were suspicious and which were not. I had seen the look in the eyes of both my doctors. I had cancer, and that was all there was to it.

The anxiety grew with each passing day of that long week. The possibilities continued to race through my mind. What would we have to do? How would I react? Would I have to take chemo? Would I have to have surgery?

I already knew what kind of chemo I would most likely have to have. I already knew I'd probably have to have thirty-plus days of radiation after a lumpectomy. I already knew I might have to have radiation after a mastectomy. I wasn't really afraid of a mastectomy at that point because approximately 80 percent of breast cancers are treated by lumpectomies followed by radiation, as long as they get clear margins—meaning, no evidence of cancer in the area surrounding where the tumor was removed.

But my mind was also numb. It was as if I was in information overload from all the things I'd ever said to my counselees. I couldn't hear myself talk. I was simply numb.

Sometimes, when we discussed different matters, Dick would ask, "What would you say to one of your patients?" I would mumble in return, "I don't know. I don't know what I'd say. I don't want to think about it." Because by saying what I would have said to my patients, it would be reality. And I was still in denial.

Finally the day of my biopsy arrived. I had hoped for an early appointment, but the procedure was scheduled for late in the day. Both of my sisters-in-law came to be with us, though Pat stayed at the house. Sharon accompanied Dick and me to the surgeon's office. As we rode the elevator, I turned to Sharon and said, "I've ridden this elevator with hundreds and hundreds of patients with unconfirmed breast cancer, but I never thought I'd be one of them."

Dick came back to the exam room with me. He watched as they deadened the skin around my breast. Dr. Corgan used an ultrasound-guided needle to get a core biopsy to find the tumor. This pierced the tumor with the needle, pulling out the tissue into its core. I could see tears rolling down Dick's cheeks as he watched the blood drip from my breast.

I swallowed and looked back at Dr. Corgan. "What do you think? Do you think it's cancer?

She leaned over the bed and looked into my eyes, answering quietly. "Yes, I do."

"I knew."

She nodded. "And I knew you knew, Debbie. Of course, we'll need to be 100 percent sure. We'll get the pathology reports back in a few days so we'll know exactly what we're dealing with. And we'll have the cytology report to give us a look at the inner workings of the tumor, then we'll go from there."

I didn't cry. But I closed my eyes against a myriad of thoughts and took a deep breath. Surgery lay immediately ahead in my future. Chemo was mostly likely in my future. Radiation was in my future. Maybe even a mastectomy. Now I was going to visit the nightmare I had talked about with hundreds of patients.

Oh, how I wish I didn't know what lies ahead . . .

But I knew.

I would see cancer from both sides now.

Chapter 2

A PRELIMINARY DIAGNOSIS

—Dick

Being around gynecologists has always made me nervous. Not that I've been around that many. Well, maybe one.

It's strange. When most guys get together and shoot the bull, the question always comes up about where they work and what they do. Ask those questions of a gynecologist and see what you get. Some guys know just enough about them to wonder why in the world any man would desire to be one.

Sure, a woman gynecologist is fine. She can relate. But a man? "Doesn't that affect his love life?" they ask.

Other guys think it's the perfect job. This subject has generated many questionable jokes and a laugh or two. Still, from my perspective, there are no clear answers.

Any word ending in "ology" means the scientific study of something. So it stands to reason that gynecology deals with the scientific study of a "gyne" or "gynecs."

Men are so stupid they think that gynecology only focuses on female anatomical components of particular interest to them. So they conclude that the medical term for these anatomical components must be "gynecs." You learn something new every day. I can picture two construction workers at lunch, eating bologna sandwiches watching a beautiful lady walk down the sidewalk. "Hey dude, take a look at those gynecs!" Or a young adolescent boy looking at the September issue of *Gynecboy* he stole from his older brother. Older brothers always seem to have a stack of those.

According to the *Online Etymology Dictionary, gyne* comes from the Greek word *gynaik,* which means "woman or female."[1] This is even more interesting. It seems that *gynecology* is basically the scientific study of a woman. Frankly, there is no scientific degree in the universe a man could earn that would make him even remotely understand a woman.

All kidding aside, gynecologists are godsends. Their job specializes in the discovery and treatment of problems in the female reproduction system. A good gynecologist is proactive and a key player in the discovery and treatment of breast cancer. Deb's gynecologist was outstanding.

I was in Dallas attending an annual leadership meeting for my missions agency when Deb called me. She had scheduled an appointment with her doctor, but I could not be there. She was concerned about the telltale lump in her left breast. Several years before, she had a slight scare when she felt an unusual lump in the same breast. A diagnostic mammogram determined that the lump was benign. Both of us hoped this exam would have the same result.

I frantically paced the hallway, playing hooky from the required meeting while I waited for Deb to call. Whether she was at the doctor or not, I still didn't mind missing another boring speaker. My boss saw me and understood. He's a great boss.

Deb called me after she left the doctor's office. Her voice quivered, and I immediately knew something was horribly wrong. Her doctor felt something in her breast too, and it did not feel right. He immediately referred her to an oncological surgeon. Deb got in to see the surgeon that afternoon.

Oncological. The word hit me like a ton of bricks. Any word or phrase including "oncology" is bad; even worse when "surgeon" follows it. Oncology means the study of tumors. Cancer is a tumor. The C-word is like the vilest of all cuss words. Previously, that C-word had only referenced someone else I, as a minister, might be praying for or visiting. Now it referred to Deb. I wasn't a minister praying for someone else. I was a husband begging God that my wife would be okay.

I was still on the plane wondering, waiting, crying, and praying when the surgeon performed the sonogram on Deb. As the doctor stared at a screen trying to decipher every line and shadow, she saw something. She didn't say it was cancer, but Deb knew by the look in her eyes. When you're around cancer for eighteen years as Deb has been, you just know. It was as if a silent diagnosis had been confirmed between two professionals. But the silence would soon become a scream.

When I arrived home late that evening, we cried, hugged, cried, and hugged. I didn't want it to be her. I'd rather it was me. Even the unofficial diagnosis was enough to make me wonder if Deb and I would grow old together. I had never thought about losing her.

The Biopsy and the Truth

I had never been to an oncological surgeon's office before, but I found it stereotypical of most other doctor's offices. It felt clinical and smelled weird . . . not a bad weird, but definitely weird. In a lame attempt to lighten the mood, I jokingly asked Deb if I could smell cancer. She smiled. "Not usually." But our moods were too heavy to be lightened.

As usual, the receptionist gave Deb a thousand pages of forms to fill out. Why do you have to tell them about your mother's cousin's sister-in-law's daughter who broke a pinky playing jacks on the driveway when she was two years old? It must be important for any future treatments.

After sharing her complete life history and a thesis on the origin of the universe, Deb returned the forms to the receptionist. Without looking up, the receptionist asked her for her insurance card. When they do this, it always makes you feel so insignificant. As if the only reason you're being treated is to boost the doctor's income. It's always scary when they ask for the card. For the briefest moment you're filled with anxiety, worried you might not have it with you. Will they shoot you if you don't? Will they let you die in there without a Xeroxed copy? We hoped not.

All the information went into her new folder. The thesis required two folders. Folders are always stored in a back room among thousands of others. Only the CIA has access to them.

After sitting for two days in the waiting room without going to the bathroom, someone said, "Debbie Church?" We felt both relief and dread: relief that part of our wait was over and dread because this was only the beginning of a longer wait.

An LPN stood at the door opened to the inner sanctum. She smiled. "How are you doing today?" Somehow, the usual reply "fine" didn't seem appropriate. We wanted to say, "Absolutely terrible. Why would we be here if she were well?"

I was so nervous. I had been dreading this examination. But no more than Deb.

I sat down on a chair in the official examination room. If I were a preschooler, the size of that chair would've been a perfect fit. Deb sat upon an examination table covered with white paper. I guess it was supposed to make the vinyl sterile, although it was only as thick as one page in a King James Bible. Surely something from the molecular level could seep up though it. We tried to be upbeat, but our smiles and jokes only masked the total fear at what might be verified.

Deb was asked to take off her shirt and bra, then put on a pink paper "blouse" that barely covered her breasts. Any other time, this would have been a fun thing for her to wear at home. She would disagree, of course. She's a full-fledged, fully-covered, fully protected pajama girl.

Deb sat there with the paper blouse almost covering her breasts. My heart was breaking for her. I wanted to cry, but my tears would only upset her more.

Please let this be a joke or a dream. Let me wake up laughing.

After waiting in this room for around ten hours, Dr. Corgan came in. I liked her the first time I saw her. She was so personable and upbeat. She looked confident and professional.

After she examined Deb's breast, she did the sonogram. I leaned forward and watched the images appearing on the monitor. *Does she see anything? Does it look bad? Is Deb okay? Is this a false alarm?*

Dr. Corgan pinpointed the location of the questionable area and did a needle biopsy. I kept praying. *Please, God, please don't let anything be wrong, especially not cancer!*

The doctor removed a small piece of tissue. I'll never forget the image of Deb lying on that table. Thin streaks of blood flowed down her left breast from the small puncture, absorbing into her paper blouse. It was so surreal.

This should not be happening, I thought. Deb does not deserve this.

But she was so brave.

As an oncology counselor, Deb knew the process and exactly what doctors can surmise without a full pathology report. "Does it look cancerous?" Deb's question filled the room with anxiety, fear, and trembling. Hope hung on every word, but barely.

"Yes."

Dr. Corgan placed the tissue sample in a small vial and labeled it *Debbie Church*. "Without a full pathology report, I can't be 100 percent sure—but maybe ninety-nine."

That was close enough. Deb knew Dr. Corgan had done thousands of biopsies like this and could usually tell.

My heart broke and fell to the floor. Life would never be the same again.

Chapter 3

I ALWAYS WANTED TO BE A DOCTOR

—*Deb*

"Point up! Stretch, girls, stretch!"

Miss Clark shouted her instructions over the rhythmic piano melody while my young ballet class eagerly followed her every word. She was beautiful, with striking red hair and the mystique that surrounds one who has danced with the Rockettes. I adored her and tried with all the muster my eight-year-old body could handle to be the best ballerina in the class.

"Plié! Plié!"

My hand clutching the barre, I slowly and gracefully bent into the familiar position, extending my tiny muscular thighs outward until they were completely horizontal. My head held high, I stole a glimpse in the mirror, catching the faint smile on Miss Clark's face as she surveyed my perfectly straight back. I felt my own smile tug at my cheeks. I was her favorite pupil.

"Very nice, girls," she announced. "Excellent! Now second position—"

I had dreamed of being a ballerina for as long as I could remember. Even as a little girl, I was mesmerized by *Swan Lake, The Nutcracker,* and *Sleeping Beauty*. I wanted to be the heroine of those storybook dreams and plays. I loved the lights and the glamour—everything right down to the costumes and the shoes. To me, ballet shoes looked as if they, too, were part of the fairy tales I dreamed about.

Little did I realize the pain and the practice that would have to accompany these diminutive pink devices of torture! As I stuffed my toes into them, I would dream of being on stage. But before you could do your first pirouette, your legs had to become like steel in order to lift your body. You must first learn to contort your arms and limbs to make strange motions, all the while making it look effortless, gliding on air to beautiful music while not betraying the fact that you were in abject pain. But as the practices continued, so did the pain, until your body got used to the punishment it received every day.

Once I remember going backstage during a performance only to notice some blood in my ballet shoes. A split callus on my toe caused it to look much worse than it really was. But it reminded me of the hours and hours of practice that are necessary before performing. It was difficult and painful, but I found it only inspired me further in the quest of my dream. If others could not or would not endure the pain, then I would.

I began entering dance contests when I was just five years old. Soon my bedroom shelves were lined with trophies, most of them engraved with First Place. By the time I was in seventh grade I was placing in city-wide and county-wide contests. My dreams of dancing in the New York City Ballet were firmly rooted, and I would let nothing stand in my way.

Nothing, that is, except a broken foot. When I was thirteen, while playing basketball, I severely injured my left foot. After four operations, it was obvious I would never dance professionally. I watched my dreams disappear.

All I ever wanted was to be the best. I was the middle daughter of three girls, and my father always told us to do the best we could—to not let anyone ever tell us we couldn't do something. I never forgot those words. I don't know that I was necessarily a Type A personality, but I always wanted to be the best at whatever I did. I loved studying and making good grades. And I loved to win.

I guess I was a weird little kid, now that I think of it. Normally it's the first-born child who has the drive to succeed. But my older sister was more into having fun, so it was only natural that I would slide into the role of the overachiever in the mix. I was going to be the perfect child.

I grew up in Fayetteville, North Carolina, where my father owned a small office supply company. We had a comfortable living, and I never thought about money. I suppose we were considered upper middle class, but I didn't know anything about that at the time. I was most definitely not a debutante, contrary to what my husband likes to say.

When my dreams of becoming a world-acclaimed ballerina didn't work out, I found a new passion: medicine! Looking back, I realize it's not surprising that I was drawn to medicine. When I was quite young, my father helped start the Cumberland County Rescue Squad. These volunteers were trained by physicians. They were paramedics before that field became a recognized profession. My father responded to wrecks and transported patients to the hospital, where he assisted the doctors, treating wounds and making stitches. (This was long before lawsuits were so common.) He brought home medical books, and I tried to read them and pretended to understand what the big words on the pages meant. He even let me use his stethoscope. I called myself Dr. Knight (my maiden name) and made house calls on all my dolls.

But I was never a healthy child. Apparently my immune system was not very strong. I was extremely skinny. Dad would say, "Eat! You look like a ragamuffin!" I seemed to get sick a lot and had to miss a lot of school. But I graduated from high school and enrolled at Salem College in Winston-Salem. It was a private women's school with only five hundred students on the campus, but I loved it. It was unique, it was small, and it was set in a Moravian community with a strong German Lutheran flavor. It reminded me a lot of Williamsburg, Virginia, though on a much smaller scale.

Salem College was founded in 1772, and we proudly boast that George Washington did, in fact, sleep at Brother's House on campus. I loved that it was so uniquely different from typical university campuses. Students had one-on-one relationships with the professors.

Of course, at a Southern women's college we were steeped in the tradition of etiquette and proper social manners. Three times a day, a four-tone chime rang out across campus, calling us to breakfast, lunch, or dinner. We ate all our meals together in a formal dining room, with linen tablecloths and fine china. We'd stand behind our chairs and say a blessing: "Come Lord Jesus, our guest is Thee, and bless these gifts bestowed by Thee." Then we'd sit down.

I truly loved Salem College and excelled there, doing some honors work along the way. I wrote articles that got published and also worked at nearby Bowman Gray Medical School. But during my sophomore year, I got sick with a severe case of bronchitis I just couldn't shake. Eventually I had to drop out for the rest of the semester. I think I was trying too hard to make straight A's so I could get into medical school. In the process I let myself get run down physically.

At that time I honestly felt that God was telling me I could not undertake the strenuous task of becoming a doctor. I simply did not have the physical stamina to do it. After a lot of prayer I reluctantly gave up that dream and dropped biology, changing my major to psychology and history—a double major to make it more challenging. But I never let go of my love of learning medicine.

I really enjoyed my psychology courses, studying human behavior. I made plans to go to graduate school and get my PhD in psychology. But about that time a friend's fiancé told me about pastoral counseling—the mixing of religion and psychology. The combination appealed to me. Following graduation I entered Southeastern Baptist Theological Seminary in Wake Forest, North Carolina, to pursue a degree in pastoral counseling.

Of course, I continued in my goal to be the best I could be, always striving to make the best grade in the class. There were three thousand men on the campus and only one hundred women. My husband tells me the only reason I made good grades was because I was attractive and blonde, "the only half-decent-looking girl on campus." Of course, I know better!

In fact, I first met Dick Church at seminary. He had already completed his master of divinity degree and was working on a master of theology. We had several classes together, but I first met him in my Pauline Eschatology class. Very romantic, don't you think? He sat in the back of the classroom. I was one of two females in the class, and the other girl was married. I knew several of his roommates, and every day I would come in and wave at them. Dick, of course, thought I was flirting with him.

In the next chapter Dick will give you his version of when we met and our first date. I'm sure it will be quite embellished, and he'll try to make himself look good. But you should first know the truth.

Now Dick thinks I was only interested in him. Wrong. When our mutual friends got together for lunch, there were actually three other guys in the group I also liked. Sadly, they were all so shy and reserved that no one ever asked me out! I thought Dick was really cute, but also really weird. He was much more shy than all the others and extremely quiet around girls, but absolutely hilarious in a group.

He finally asked me out, but it was just two days before a huge Hebrew exam. I almost turned him down because I had so much studying I needed to do to prepare for the test. Regardless, I said yes, and it's a good thing. He later told me that if I had turned him down, he would never have asked me out again. And, oh, what a first date it was—motorcycle gang Christmas party.

Unfortunately the party was in Dick's hometown in Concord, a two-hour drive from Wake Forest. That meant my entire Saturday would be consumed with this trip, leaving me precious little time to study on Sunday. But I'd agreed to go, so off we went. When we arrived in Concord, we stopped by to see his parents. When I first met his mom, she cried. Not a good sign. But apparently she was distraught over some extended-family issues and, thankfully, not upset about meeting me.

At the party Dick sang carols with made-up lyrics and played his guitar. The crowd loved him. And soon, so did I. Not long after, he started writing songs for me. And I began to accompany him when he sang at local pubs or churches. We became inseparable.

The next July, on my birthday, I was doing clinical pastoral education at Bowman Gray Medical Center when Dick came to see me. He took me out to dinner, and that evening he proposed. We were married the following December.

After I finished seminary, we moved to Nashville because Dick had had a song published. We began traveling all over while he pursued a singing career. In the meantime, I had two miscarriages. We eventually ended up back in Fayetteville, North Carolina, where Dick worked for my father. Dad wanted to give us his office supply business, but Dick's heart was not in the business world.

Instead, we moved to Clearwater, Florida, where we had some good friends. We rented a home from them, and Dick went to work as a commercial artist. A man of many, many talents. We began attending the First Baptist Church of Indian Rocks, and not long afterward, the pastor hired Dick as minister of education.

About this time, I got pregnant for the third time. Again I had problems and was put on strict bed rest. But in the summer of 1985, God blessed us with the birth of our son, Scott. Three years later, He blessed us with our daughter, Mary.

After serving on the staff at Indian Rocks for five years, Dick was offered a job on staff at a large metropolitan church in Fort Lauderdale. It was not the Camelot experience he had hoped for. Personalities and chemistry clashed, and Dick became absolutely miserable. He had to leave to keep what was left of his sanity.

So in just over a year, we moved to Knoxville, Tennessee, where Dick served on staff at a small church. Luckily we were called back 'home' again to a church in Clearwater, Florida—home because this is where our children were born. Calvary Baptist Church became our Camelot for five years. Those were some of the happiest days of our lives.

After our return to Clearwater, I happened to be looking at the want ads in the newspaper when I saw a job opening for a female oncology counselor, requiring a masters of divinity degree. Women with an MDiv degree are not that common, so I knew it was a God thing. I had worked in clinical pastoral education at Bowman Gray, sometimes on the oncology ward. I got the job and went back into oncology. I loved it from day one.

My office was on the oncology floor of the hospital. I took part in chart rounds with all the physicians and head nurse at 6:30 each morning. They loved my involvement, and so did I.

My schedule required some juggling on the home front. Dick took the kids to school each morning, and I'd leave work at three o'clock so I could pick them up. My best friend's daughter was a classmate of Scott's. She would report on his day for me—how he'd cried if he didn't get all A's. Apparently it's true about the apple not falling far from the tree. Mary would be sitting on the pavement, her hair and bow still a mess from her father's sad attempts to fix her hair that morning. (Doing hair is not one of his aforementioned many talents.)

Those were good times. Those days were special. Some of the best years of our lives.

I absolutely loved working with cancer patients. They overcome such amazing obstacles. First finding out that they have cancer, then all the different stages of cancer—not unlike the stages of grief—and continuing. Physically, emotionally, spiritually—so many obstacles, yet they keep moving forward.

Over the years, I discovered my main job was simply to take them by the hand and help them down that difficult road because it's such a unique disease. It's a literal rollercoaster. One day you feel fine, the next you feel awful. But I loved helping them and their families and getting to know each of them personally.

It's also a chronic disease these days. Over the years we've come so far in development of chemo and different protocols to treat cancer. And it's become the place where I can lend a hand and help these individuals and their families through some of the most difficult times in their lives.

People like Mr. Rhodes, my prostate cancer patient. From his first diagnosis, he had great hope and anticipation that the treatment would be a complete cure. But after two years he returned because it had spread to his bladder and his bowels, a Stage IV disease. He did go through the initial treatment but later decided against any more chemo. The doctors urged me to try to change his mind, but he'd already made up his mind. He didn't want to live out the rest of his life in so much pain.

Sometimes it's hard for doctors to see the other side of the equation because they are trained to heal at all costs. I was often stuck in the middle. Even Mrs. Rhodes wanted me to change her husband's mind. In the end, she acquiesced, understanding the pain and discomfort he was experiencing. He was hospitalized and died before we were able to admit him to Hospice.

That's not unusual. When a patient decides not to pursue more treatment, they often die soon after. There's a fine line there between the spiritual aspect of God's timing for you to die and determining you want no more treatment. I think they just know. They're listening intently to their bodies, and they know.

The family tried so hard to hold on to Mr. Rhodes. But once they accepted his decision, they all seemed to have peace about it. He was such a good and kind man, and theirs was a very gentle family. By the time I returned that evening, Mr. Rhodes had already died. His wife and two daughters were still there, along with his son who had finally arrived. It was as if his father had waited for him to get there and was finally able to rest and let go.

When I walked into the room, his son was crying silently there beside his father. Such a special family, making those tough decisions. Guiding them along the way wasn't easy. Just two days before, Mr. Rhodes had been sitting up, chatting with everyone, and now he was gone.

As difficult and sad as these encounters are, I love being able to help families through the journey. But never did I think I'd have to walk down that Road of Cancer myself.

Chapter 4

REVEREND CHURCH

—Dick

Reverend Church. Now there's a title. Most people think I'm kidding. I've taught countless seminars and preached in numerous churches where the introduction always includes some humorous reference to my being a minister with Church as a last name.

"Boy, you were meant to be a preacher!"

"I'm glad your parents didn't give you a first name like Baptist!"

I just laugh, but deep down I wish my last name was Smith or Jones.

One of my seminary professors read through the new roster of class members, and when he came to mine, he paused and said, "Where is Brother Church?"

Knowing what would happen, I reluctantly looked up. "Now that's a fine ecclesiastical name!" he declared. The class laughed. "No, my name is Smith," I quipped.

Believe it or not, my sister married a man with the last name of Chappell (pronounced chapel). Now she is known as Pat Church Chappell. Whenever I'm introduced, I tell them about my sister's name to take the emphasis off me. It's always better to embarrass my sister. She's older than I am, and, after all, I'm the baby of the family so I can get away with it.

I've heard it all: Reverend. Right Reverend. Most Reverend. The Good Reverend. The Very Reverend. Personally, I like the Very Reverend. But I'd like others to put all of them together when referencing me. "Ladies and gentlemen, I would like to introduce you to The Most, Good, Right, and Very Reverend Church." But they'd still laugh, and it would be rather vain, I suppose. I wonder if they called Jesus Reverend?

The term goes way back. According to the *Online Etymology Dictionary*, it is a form of address for clergymen dating back to 1485.[1] The abbreviation Rev. became acceptable in 1721. Why it took them 236 years to shorten it, no one knows. But it must have something to do with being burned at the stake or blasphemy. Titles meant everything back in the Middle Ages.

Reverend means "worthy to be revered; entitled to reverence."[2] Reverence means "a feeling or attitude of deep respect tinged with awe . . ."[3] I like the "tinged with awe." Now that is awesome. But these definitions must be referring to someone else. I can't stand the pressure of "awe." To use "deep respect" for me is stretching it a bit too. But it's nice to know the word *reverend* is used in only one place in the Bible (Psalm 111:9, KJV). In context it references the essence of God, not man. Man is never called reverend in the Bible. God is the only One worthy of that title.

Yes, I am a reverend. It became official back in 1986. In the Baptist churches I have served, a person becomes a reverend through ordination. In those churches, as with most other Baptists, ordination is simply a church's affirmation given to a person who has been called of God to ministry. A church can ordain whomever they choose. However, some Baptist groups limit ordination to men only. Typically it involves the laying on of hands, a symbolic gesture of affirmation and blessing.

The First Baptist Church of Indian Rocks in Largo, Florida, ordained me. Deb and I had attended the church for three years, and what a great experience I had there. I loved the church and the pastor.

Appearing before an ordination council can be quite intimidating. My council consisted of twelve men, both ordained and non-ordained. Deacons, Sunday school teachers, lawyers, retirees, staff members, a couple of other reverends from different churches, and my pastor all sat on the council.

Prior to my appearance, I prepared a document outlining my theological positions on the fundamentals of the faith, such as what I believed about God, Jesus, the Holy Spirit, salvation, sin, grace, eschatology, biblical inspiration, and so on. In order to ensure my mental stability and theological accuracy, they required me to submit this information. And, of course, they needed to agree I would not embarrass the church. Each member received a copy of my position paper.

This happened at 3:30 on a Sunday afternoon. No one comes to church at 3:30 on Sunday afternoon. This is prime nap time. Even the pastor is usually asleep. But on this day fresh meat awaited. Council members salivated, awake and starving like a bunch of Pavlovian dogs.

I waited in an adjacent room with walls too thick to hear anything. I pressed my ear so hard against the sheet rock that the anvil and stirrup changed places. I anticipated possible questions. I wanted all of them to be easy. What is your favorite color? Where were you born? What's your last name? I could breeze through the first two. The last one, I would answer Smith or Jones.

The council thoroughly reviewed my exhaustive theological position paper. It took less than five minutes. As with a Senate or House bill, no one probably read it. They wanted a nap.

One of my staff member friends on the council opened the door. He smiled hungrily. "You're on." I swear I saw slobber drooling down the corner of his mouth as he anticipated a bloody and voluptuous feast.

I entered a small room and sat in front of men seated in folding chairs arranged in a semicircle. I felt like a target in a spiritual firing range. I never like sitting in semicircles. It makes me very uncomfortable. It screams audience participation and interaction. I have to talk with someone. I prefer theater seating. It indicates "Leave me alone; I just want to listen."

The grilling began with prayer. I wonder if they pray before executions? Most everything in church begins with prayer, even bathroom breaks.

Most of the old guys fidgeted uncomfortably on the metal chairs. I witnessed eighty-year-old butts compressed between two hundred pounds of midsection and a thin piece of sheet metal. They repeatedly glanced at their watches, shifted from cheek to cheek, and looked mad. Only at church do people sit in metal chairs. Can you imagine coming home from a long day of work to relax on a folding chair? "Honey, get me a glass of tea and another metal chair to put my feet on. I'm exhausted."

Suffice it to say all went well. The council approved my ordination unanimously. An unframed certificate of ordination followed hugs and handshakes. Each man signed his name as evidence.

An elaborate ordination ceremony in my honor occurred two Sundays later. Laying-on of the hands followed songs and preaching.

(Sounds weird, doesn't it?) Debbie stood by my side through it all. We'd been married about eight years at the time.

Prior to all the pomp and circumstance, I graduated from Southeastern Baptist Theological Seminary in Wake Forest, North Carolina, with a master of divinity degree. Jesus must have had that degree too. After all, He's divine, right?

How did I get to seminary and ordination? What made me decide to go into the ministry? I have been a minister for twenty-five years, and sometimes I still wonder . . .

Some men are "Mama-called and Daddy-sent" into the ministry. They enter the ministry to please Mom, out of some sort of guilt, then Dad pays their seminary tuition. I know some of these folks, and trust me, I did not fall among their ranks. As a young boy, that would have been the last thing I desired.

I don't know when I first started to think about the possibility. I do remember talking about it a few times with my granny when I was around eleven years old. I attended her church and heard about being a missionary or a preacher or a Christian teacher. That sparked my imagination. I thought it would be neat to go into some dark part of Africa and dodge the darts of hungry cannibals just to tell them about Jesus. But then, I wondered, if they ate me, would I taste like chicken? Seems like I felt a little nudge back then. But maybe it was the candy Granny fed me in church.

I accepted Jesus as my Savior when I was eleven. I "walked the aisle" and "prayed the sinner's prayer" with my pastor, Rev. Floyd Willis. Walking the aisle in a Baptist church usually indicates a person is responding to an invitation by the pastor to come to Jesus. Walking the aisle, however, is quite unnecessary. You may have watched a Billy Graham crusade and witnessed the massive crowds walking the stadium aisles. And most pastors agree that if it's good enough for Billy, it's good enough for me! But Billy did not invent the tradition. Rather, it was Charles Finney back in the early 1800s who first invited people to come forward in altar calls.

I displayed very little Christ-likeness during high school. I drank a few beers here and there, and some considered me the captain of the drinking team. My team lost every Friday and Saturday night.

After high school I attended Wingate College in North Carolina. By the end of my sophomore year, I made a commitment to follow Jesus much more closely. We Baptists call it rededication. I got involved in various Christian groups and studied the Bible in detail. I taught and preached at many churches and felt a certain confirmation that I was going in the right direction.

After Wingate I entered the art program at East Carolina University in Greenville, North Carolina. As a talented drawer, it seemed like the logical thing to do. But I had a restless spirit, and my life seemed unfulfilled. After praying, reading the Bible, talking to pastors, performing and enjoying ministerial-type duties, and receiving a certain amount of confirmation from other Christians (that is the general sequence, I've been told), I made the leap of faith. I dropped out of East Carolina and went back home where I commuted to the University of North Carolina at Charlotte to earn a BA in religion. Then I enrolled in seminary.

Please understand, I believe each Christian is called to the ministry, whether his profession is doctor, lawyer, roofer, or other. Some say that every believer in any job is called full-time, and I agree. But the call I am referring to here is full-time, not part-time while holding another job.

At seminary I studied the Bible and prepared for a career in ministry. I didn't know exactly what ministry I was called to. I was open to being a pastor, educator, teacher, or wherever I felt God opened a door. But a career in ministry seemed secondary when my eyes fell upon a beautiful blonde girl named Debbie.

Here's how it happened, and I swear it is the truth.

At Southeastern Baptist Theological Seminary in Wake Forest, North Carolina, the ratio between men and women had to be at least twenty guys to one gal. Most fellows pranced and danced around them like animals performing some kind of evolutionary mating ritual. For the record, I never pranced or danced. The fun of camping or mountain climbing filled my weekends. I liked the ladies (trust me), but I wasn't actively looking for one.

The seminary provided students with a pictorial directory. It showed pictures of all the seminarians. Most single guys frantically searched each page, trying to find a girl—a pulse the only qualification.

My eyes fell upon a certain picture as I casually reviewed the directory one day. Debbie Knight from Fayetteville, North Carolina, leaped off the page. A weird and quite unexpected thought immediately entered my mind: *Here is the girl you are going to marry.* I laughed. *Yeah, right,* I said to myself. I quickly dismissed it and didn't think about it again until a few months later.

I saw her. I recognized the blonde hair as she entered the Johnson Building for one of her classes. I remembered the thought I'd had while looking at her picture and chuckled. *Yeah, right, there's the girl I'm going to marry.* She was attractive, but I wasn't looking. I dismissed it again and went to my class in another building.

About a month later, I became a friend-of-a-friend of Debbie's. One day I went to lunch with my friend-of-a-friend, and Debbie joined us. *Gosh, she's beautiful!* I said to myself. Since I am very shy, I didn't say much. After a brief introduction, I asked about her favorite color and her place of birth. I already knew her last name. I introduced myself as Dick Smith. Not really!

I began looking forward to these gatherings. We would meet for lunch as a group, but from my perspective, I ate with Deb and no one else. My conversation with her began to extend beyond colors and birthplaces. Still extremely shy, I didn't ask her out after several lunches. I wanted to so badly. I felt like a pure idiot. She hinted from time to time that she would like to go see a certain movie with me, but I never took the bait.

I finally got the nerve and invited her to a motorcycle club Christmas party two-and-a-half hours away from campus for our first date. The club met in my hometown of Concord, North Carolina, and that evening, I would be the entertainment, playing the guitar and singing funny songs.

Now that must have sounded strange and even a little dangerous to her. I explained that the club did not consist of bearded men with tattoos and women who flashed from time to time while riding on the back of Harleys. The Cabarrus Cycle Club consisted of lawyers, civic workers, and the like. They rode Honda and Yamaha bikes.

When Deb told her father about her plans to accompany a guy to a motorcycle club party, he said, "You're what?! You will not go to a motorcycle gang!" She explained it was primarily old men. But then she added, "He is a little weird though."

One date led to others. I grew less shy. Gradually, we came to the I-like-you stage, followed by the I-like-you-a-lot stage. Then we graduated to the I-love-you stage. And I did and still do.

Deb and I exchanged wedding vows on December 30, 1978. As with many newlywed couples, we experienced a rough beginning. I had to learn important things such as not leaving the toilet seat up. She almost drowned in there once.

We had to learn how to communicate and fight right. I unpacked my past, and she did too. From time to time it seemed as if we spoke foreign languages to each other, but I learned her love language, and she learned mine. I'm still learning, but I now score an A on the toilet issue—well, maybe a B minus.

I have been a hospital patient only twice in my life, the first time for a tonsillectomy when I was five years old. The second came after we married. Chest pain and Deb made me go to a doctor. I shouldn't have gone. To avoid being sued if I died on the way back home, he checked me into the hospital and found only a muscular/skeletal issue. My heart checked out fine.

Deb, on the other hand, has had several difficult times throughout her life. Pain is not new to her. She stayed as active as any kid, but she battled stomach ulcers as a child. Because of a basketball injury on her foot during high school, she required surgery. Bone fragments left after her first foot surgery resulted in several more operations over ten years.

During the first year of our marriage, she had her final foot surgery, a rather extensive and painful one. The doctor placed a very large cast over her entire leg, from high up on the hip, to the tip of her toes. The cast weighed so much she needed a sling around her neck that attached to the bottom of the cast. This kept it off the floor when she walked or stood with crutches.

Now the caregiver, I had to do everything. I cooked, cleaned, and ran errands. Each night I placed her into the bathtub. (I enjoyed that caregiving duty.) I made sure her cast remained out of the water. I positioned her so that her leg dangled up and off to one side of the tub. Being totally helpless at this point, she remained at my disposal. I left her in there a couple of times until the water got cold, just to play a joke. It made her mad. At least I got to bathe her . . . a little.

Years later, she had gall bladder surgery and two miscarriages. In 1983 we moved to Clearwater, Florida. I did not immediately enter the ministry but worked various jobs, still a bit confused by the impact seminary had made upon me. I did not take that leap yet.

Back in the 1970s when I attended Southeastern Seminary, the influence of liberal theologians and scholarship impacted the curriculum, challenging the basic foundational beliefs of most conservative Christians. The professors, though brilliant, challenged students to question the inspiration of the Bible, the resurrection of Jesus, the authenticity of some of His sayings in the Gospels, among many other issues.

These teachings, so very different from what I had been taught in Sunday school, confused me somewhat. Now, looking back, I can see how I benefited from these challenges as they helped me deal more logically and reasonably with these questions. As a result, I am firmer today in what I believe and how to discuss these issues intellectually with others who question their beliefs. But it took me about two years to "get my head screwed on right." (Some would argue I'm still a bit screwed up!)

While in Clearwater, I had the opportunity to serve on staff at a wonderful church. I was serving in Paradise. Life in sunny Florida is defined by the weather, the palm trees, the sun and beach, and a sense of carefree living. We experienced some of the happiest days of our lives there.

Our kids are Crackers—meaning true Floridians—not transplants or snowbirds. They have the birth certificates to prove it. Scott is our first, and Mary is our second. Two are plenty! What handfuls.

While Scott took forever to make his appearance at birth, Mary popped out in a couple of hours. Deb and I held our perfect and beautiful baby for a few minutes until they took her away to do whatever it is they do to newborn babes.

An hour or so after Mary's birth, Deb started to hemorrhage. She began losing blood—pints of it. She turned white, and her skin looked pasty and transparent. Being so weak, she could not lift her arms or squeeze my hand.

Unknown to us at the time, her uterus had been torn. The placenta had been attached to scar tissue on the uterus caused by one of her previous miscarriages. When it separated, it tore a hole. It happened so quickly. The bed sheets looked like a murder scene on *Forensic Files,* and I panicked. I could only scream for the nurse. The nurse looked at Deb and rushed to get the gynecologist.

As they wheeled her toward the operating room, I ran by her side, holding her hand until the big double door closed in front of me. I had no time to pray with her. All alone and confused, I cried. When I called, my friends from church came to be with me. I thought for sure she was dying.

Deb's memory of the entire event is vivid. She remembers the ride into the operating room. She remembers the surgeon leaning over and looking at her, then telling the anesthesiologist, "Hurry, get her under! We're losing her!" She heard the anesthesiologist's reply: "I can't! She is not stable enough."

But even during all the trauma, Deb said she experienced perfect peace. While lying on the operating table as the doctors barked orders back and forth, she said she saw and felt a very warm and bright light. Then, out of that light, she saw the face of Jesus. He said to her in a soothing voice, "Don't worry, Debbie. Everything is going to be okay." And it was.

Deb told me that amazing story even though she was concerned I would question her sanity. She knew it had happened to her, a very real and personal experience. So, of course, being a reverend, I had to ask a very logical question: "What did He look like?" She tried to explain in great detail, but her words could not adequately explain the beauty of that moment. I believed her, and I always will. Even today, facing cancer, she is still comforted by that memory.

A minister's life is not easy. My entire family and I lived in an aquarium—fishes with people watching our every move. Ministers are constantly evaluated and judged by their congregations. So are wives and children. Some "Christians" can be very cruel. I find that sad. No family is perfect. But we sure did our best, and Deb and I always allowed our children to be regular *children*, not preacher's kids. If the church didn't like it, too bad.

In a following chapter on faith, I go into great detail about what it's like to be a minister who deals with unanswerable questions about pain and suffering. But when it becomes personal, it's an entirely different ball game. I tried to be honest.

Deb has been my greatest supporter, encourager, believer, and strength. She has seen the good, the bad, and the ugly. She has witnessed pure hypocrisy in me without being my judge and jury. She has celebrated the victories and always brought out the good in me.

As I mentioned at the first of this chapter, reverend means, "worthy to be revered; entitled to reverence." I disagree. This definition does not describe a reverend, or especially me. It defines Debbie Church.

Now that tinges me with awe!

Chapter 5

THE STAGES OF CANCER

—Deb

W e all go through stages of grief throughout our lives. I grieved when I had to stop taking ballet. I grieved when I left home for college. (I was one of those rare kids who liked home!) I even remember grieving through post-partum depression, but not for the reasons you might think.

I didn't have my children until I was thirty, and I found myself grieving over the freedoms I had lost. Sleepless nights and crying babies had replaced the relatively free life I'd led. I loved my children, but I had also loved my freedom to go and do as I please. Perhaps most new mothers experience this at one time or another, but it was a difficult situation for me to face.

Still, it's not uncommon for us to grieve at various times in our lives, especially whenever changes come along. We may not always recognize it as grief, but often that's exactly what it is. And that's why I always explain to my patients how similar cancer is to the stages of grief.

In her 1969 bestseller *On Death and Dying*, Dr. Elisabeth Kübler-Ross first detailed the five stages individuals go through when they encounter grief in their lives:

1. Denial (includes shock and isolation): *This can't be happening to me!*
2. Anger: *Why is this happening to me?*
3. Bargaining: *I promise I'll be a better person if . . .*
4. Depression (sadness): *I don't care anymore.*
5. Acceptance: *I'm ready for whatever comes.*[1]

I would assure my patients that they wouldn't necessarily go through these stages in a perfect continuum. It's more of a back-and-forth process.

All through life we find ourselves in these various stages, whether it's through a divorce, the loss of a job, or the loss of a loved one. Cancer is a disease that affects all areas of life, much like the process we experience when someone has died. Why? Because even with the medical advances, in most people's minds cancer still causes death.

We envision the hundreds of people we have seen with bald heads. We remember our friend's tough struggle or a prayer request at church about someone who has just lost a family member to cancer. The quality of cancer care has improved exponentially over the past few years, but the fears relating to cancer seem only to increase as public awareness grows at the same time.

When I was first diagnosed with cancer, I felt like I was living right for the moment. I was on the fast track of blood tests, CAT scans, MRIs and PET scans. Everything around me intensified. Even my emotions became stronger, from happiness and love to sadness and fear.

You start down this Road of Cancer, a difficult road, one you don't want to know about. But you learn about all these medical procedures, and, oh mercy, how much all this costs! And it's absolutely frightening.

The whole concept of time becomes magnified, and suddenly you're grieving. You want to go back to the day before you found your cancer. You want it to not be true! You're grieving for the person you used to be, the person who didn't have cancer. Because you don't want to do any of this!

The shock is shattering. That first realization that you have CANCER is indescribable. Of all people, I should have known better, but I could not face it. And I didn't. But it was always there in my thoughts. I wouldn't allow myself to feel all the feelings, to cry, or to be sad or angry. I simply pushed those feelings back and out of the way until I was ready to face them. I'd always been an Olympic champion at the art of pushing stuff back. For years, that's how I had coped.

Besides, I hated medical attention. I hated being the one who's sick. I liked being there for others, but I didn't want to be the one going to the doctor, having the blood work. I did not want to be there. So I chose denial.

Some choose denial and never move beyond it. Though not many, these women refuse to acknowledge they have cancer, as if ignoring the lumps they find in their breasts will somehow make them go away. In rare cases, their breasts literally turn black with necrosis. Some actually allow breast cancer to kill them rather than get help.

I finally stepped out of the fog of denial the night after I'd seen my surgeon. When I allowed the emotions to surface, they rushed over me in a torrent. The anger, the sadness, the tears, and the fear overwhelmed me.

I fell to my knees and cried out, "How can this be happening to me?!" Even though I'd known for weeks it was true, it was only then that I gave myself permission to feel these feelings. I was like a child hoping and wishing it would all go away.

Once you start on that treadmill of diagnosis and staging, you know it's real. *What's next? When will I have surgery?* Your thoughts run away with you. In my case, my knowledge was detrimental. Usually we tell our patients, "Knowledge is power. It frees you to take the necessary steps and precautions." But for me, knowledge was damaging. I understood the medical procedures coming next.

One of the worst moments came when I had my lymph nodes removed. I'd already had a biopsy. This surgery was done to determine if lymph nodes were involved because that would determine the regiment of chemo I would be given. When I woke up, they told me they'd sent off eleven nodes. Two of my sentinel lymph nodes were positive for cancer, and two more looked very suspicious. My actual tumor size was more than five centimeters.

I cried at the news because I knew too much. I would have to have chemo, radiation, a port. I had seen the side effects of the chemo, the hours it would take. This monstrous beast had attacked my immune system. The days ahead were already mapped out for me. Again, my knowledge took me too far down the road and much too soon, making it so much harder to accept the journey I was about to begin.

Fear started creeping in. Not the fear of dying. The fear was knowing how bad I was going to feel in the next few months. I just couldn't face it. I kept begging God, "Please don't make me go down this road. I don't want to do this!"

I guess I did bargain with God about my condition, though at first it didn't cross my mind that's what I was doing. You plan as much as you can as you begin to start down this road. You bargain with the doctors and the treatment and the nurses who are giving the treatment. *Please don't make it too hard for me.*

But my hardest days came before I started my chemotherapy regimen. I would have Adriamycin and Cytoxan followed by Taxol. Over the years, I'd imparted all this knowledge and information to my patients to give them comfort and to assure them that somebody knew what they were going through and what was ahead for them. They seemed to grasp hold of that assurance and hang on for dear life. I was their reassurance. But now I was the patient. And I didn't want to know any of it. My only reassurance came from Dick and my family, my extended family and friends, and from God.

With the chemo came the suffering. A patient once told me it took her all day to crawl to the bathroom. Now it was me taking all day to crawl to the bathroom. I remember other patients telling me that they would lie in bed, staring out the window for hours and hours. Now I was the one lying in bed, staring out the window for hours and hours.

They'd told me, "I feel so bad I can't even watch TV or read a book." And now I understood. As a healthy counselor, I never fully comprehended what they were talking about, though I thought I did. Now all those conversations flooded my mind so vividly, and the grief seemed unbearable.

I remember receiving cards from my friends. Sometimes all I could do was to stare at them, read over a couple of lines, and try to hold on to the fact that someone somewhere was praying for me, thinking about me, and sending me their love. Dick would keep me updated on postings from CaringBridge.org, an online source that provides free Web sites for those in the midst of health crises. "You had a thousand hits on your page today!" he'd tell me, then read some of the messages people had left for me there. He knew it always lifted my spirits.

With all those feelings of desperation, especially following the removal of eleven lymph nodes, I knew the Road of Cancer I would soon be traveling down. I saw before me the faces of my patients with each of their stories, and I didn't want to go there. I remembered how violently sick Phyllis was all through her chemo. I remembered how Susie struggled when she lost her hair. I remembered how Jane collapsed when her husband left her. Would my husband ever think about leaving me? Their stories consumed me, swirling in my head as I wondered which components of their stories would now weave their way into my story. Which would happen to me?

That's why I cried. I knew what was coming. I understood all too well.

Believe it or not, there were other times I laughed.

After her experience with chemo, Linda once told me, "Adriamycin will kick your butt!" (This chemotherapy drug is known as the Red Devil because of its horrendous side effects.) One day during chemo when I felt so bad that I remembered Linda's comment, I laughed out loud. "You're right, Linda. Adriamycin really does kick your butt!"

Then there was the night Dick tried to cut my hair. Just two weeks after my second chemo, my hair was falling out by the handfuls. And with each handful, I cried more. He tried so hard to help that night, but the result looked pitiful.

If I hadn't been so heartbroken, I would have laughed. I looked like a ragamuffin! Out of desperation he called his stylist and asked if she would shave my head for me. She graciously agreed and didn't even charge us for doing it. I remember being sick as a dog as she shaved off the rest of my hair.

It's the process of becoming bald that's so hard. Once the hair is gone, you're resigned to it. Over the years, lots of women have told me it was more traumatic for them to lose their hair than to lose their breasts. That was not the case for me, but losing your hair is a big step because it truly identifies you as a cancer patient. It's your first stigma.

For me, it wasn't that bad, especially when I found a nice wig. In fact, I started a family trend. As soon as I began wearing a wig, my two sisters-in-law decided they'd try on some wigs themselves. Now they're never without them! I take full credit for their new look! I also wore lots of hats when I went out—ball caps, floppy straw hats, all kinds. Plus Dick was so accepting about me going around the house without my wig on. That was the best freedom. And it made all the difference.

One of the funniest stories I've ever heard from a patient happened one day as I talked with Cindy about the difficulties of sex as a cancer patient. She looked at me with tears in her eyes and said, "I love my husband. And I understand his needs are still there, even if mine aren't. That's why, right now, all we're having is mercy sex."

Mercy sex! What a brilliant name for it! Even though I completely understood what she said, (and now even more so), I still chuckle every time I think about it. Dick has a lot to say about this in another chapter, so stay tuned!

I believe cancer patients go through every single aspect of all the stages of grief. Personally, I'm not yet at total acceptance of my disease. Even today at the dentist, I realized I'm not yet there. When the hygienist asked if I'd had any medical issues they should know about, I had to laugh. "You could say that."

As I went through the litany of everything that had happened to me, it felt like I was talking about one of my patients. Not me! On my way home, I realized I'm still in a stage of denial. I also realized that everything has not yet been redeemed. It's still a process.

The sadness and depression comes in waves, less and less as time goes by. I'm having fewer episodes of anger now. The fear lessens at times, though it often sneaks up on me when I least expect it. Unfortunately, because I've been so good at denial and "stuffing" all my life, I started having anxiety attacks. They're very real, and when they hit I'm very fearful, even though there's never a specific cause I can pinpoint. I have no idea what brings them on—only something I must have stuffed down deep inside at some other point.

The anxiety attacks started at the very beginning of my diagnosis and kept getting worse. Initially they came upon me late in the afternoon or in the evening when so many thoughts from the day crossed my mind. Sometimes a commercial would come on TV, awakening a concern or a memory. Sometimes patients would call me late at night wanting to talk about their fears, triggering some of my own.

For many of my patients, the anxiety attacks don't surface until all the treatments are over. That's when they feel as if they've been left all alone. Before, they had all those weekly appointments to check their vital signs, blood tests to monitor their progress, even chemo or radiation treatments to kill the wretched disease. *Someone's watching over me, making sure everything is okay.* After the last treatment, they're excited, but the realization hits them: *It's just me now! I'm all alone now.*

It reminds me of a joke Billy Graham often told. A man had fallen off a cliff and was hanging by a root. He cried out, "Help! Is anyone there? Please help me!" God answered him. "Yes, son, I'm here. I'll save you. Just let go." The man paused, thinking. Finally he shouts, "Anyone else up there?"

We don't want to let go. Our physicians, our nurses, our treatments give us a sense of security. But when they tell us to come back in three months, we feel as though they have let us go. "Anybody else up there?"

Therefore, you realize the fears don't end when treatment ends. You continue to have check-ups every three months the first year after your treatment ends. And each time, the day before you go, you're scared to death. *Will everything be all right? What are they going to find?* If any problems come up, you're terrified. Like the time my breast swelled up with blood and fluid because I'd been too active.

Anything that happens to your body frightens you. Because I know breast cancer can spread to the liver, the brain, the lungs, and the bones, whenever I feel the slightest ache or pain in my body or get dizzy, my heart starts to flutter with fear. *Could it be back?*

The stages of grief jump back and forth. Often the sadness and depression comes and goes. It's important to recognize these stages as they come and go, or you may be accosted by these anxiety attacks. Since I didn't have a counselor, I learned that talking with friends or Dick always helped. But it wasn't easy. I've always been the counselor, the giver. To be on the taking side was hard for me. But I had to learn how to be the receiver because so many times I had absolutely nothing to give or offer others. Not even one shred of patience.

Without exception, the biggest issue I face with my cancer patients is the fear of recurrence. With every anniversary date, every follow-up exam, and every blood test comes that haunting resurgence of fear. Most people simply don't know how to deal with it. In support groups I've led, I always ask my patients how they cope with this fear. Most say time is the best healer. The longer you go without recurrence, the safer you feel. It sounds so simplistic, but for many it's the only thing that helps put that fear to rest.

Even though cancer does not equal death, especially with all the successful treatments we now have, the idea of death does enter your mind. People still die from cancer. From the counseling end, my perspective is skewed because I see so many patients in their late-term cancer diagnosis. That's when they need counseling and their families need help. They're desperate to know how to get through this. In addition, many of those I saw on a regular basis were the ones not doing well. For them, death was most likely just around the corner.

For me, thinking about death isn't difficult, because I am truly not afraid to die. My faith in God and my Savior Jesus Christ allows me that reassurance. I just don't want to leave the family and friends I so dearly love.

But even though I'm not afraid, life on "the other side" is still ambiguous. Even the strongest of Christians are often frightened as they take their last breath. But I am sure God will be with me. Throughout life, I have found His guidance and presence. It is His strong hand that reaches down to bring me back up. Sometimes I don't feel it at that moment. But by looking back, I know He was and is there.

The stage of acceptance is different for every individual. And it doesn't necessarily mean they've accepted everything. It just means they realize that they're not in control. For me, I know that's true because it's God who's in control—not me. And with that comes a sense of peace and assurance that no matter what happens, He's there and He's in control.

Even knowing that God is in control, there's still a degree of fear in your gut. "Then why do I have cancer?" I'm not sure I like giving up my control. But it's an illusion that we have control over anything. I've only semi-accepted this knowledge.

When I was in seminary, my Hebrew professor taught one of the most beautiful lessons I've ever heard. Dr. Scoggins previously taught Hebrew in Israel where he also took part in a number of archeological digs. In this particular lesson, he made Psalm 23 come to life.

He taught us the real message of that psalm, explaining how the shepherd knew each of his sheep intimately—which ones didn't follow well, which ones tended to wander off toward the rocky places instead of the safer paths, which ones were prone to falling on their backs and almost drowning while they drank from lake water (sheep aren't very bright!), and all of their unique characteristics. They were all different, yet he knew each one of them and knew how best to care for them individually.

I love the analogy of the shepherd lovingly caring for his sheep because throughout the Old Testament, God has called us His sheep. Even Jesus referred to us as sheep. Jesus asked Simon Peter three times if he loved Him, then said, "Feed my sheep" (John 21:17). Even through the valley of the shadow of death, the shepherd protected his sheep. Danger lurked all around for his sheep—be it wolves and other predators or steep cliffs. He was always there for them.

How comforted we are to have a Shepherd who guards us even through the valley of the shadow of death. I have walked in that valley now. "The shadow of death" lurks in your mind. It is passing over you now. Death may not yet be a reality; for now it's just the shadow of what is yet to come. But when you have cancer, there are many moments you feel as if you live in that shadow.

Often when I talk about the shadow of death, I hear people say things like, "Anyone can die, at any time. It doesn't just happen to cancer patients." Yes, that's true. I could die tomorrow in a car accident. But living with cancer is a different kind of shadow of death. It's never totally out of your periphery. That's why Psalm 23:4 is so comforting. "Even though I walk through the valley of the shadow of death, I will fear no evil for you are with me." It is such a comfort for me to get to that point where I can accept the promise of the Shepherd to guide and protect me. It's where I am now.

Some of my patients never arrive at the threshold of acceptance. "Nancy" wasn't in full-time denial, but she never reached the stage of acceptance. Cancer free for more than eight years, she never once found peace. Today she still suffers psychologically, tormented around the clock with fear and irrational assumptions. Nothing has helped. I've tried every behavioral therapy modification, and she's on several medications to no avail. Once she cried all night after reading one of her doctor's reports, completely misunderstanding the information written on its pages. Her heart rate jumped to 135 before she found out it was all a mistake.

Such unresolved grief and fear takes a toll. Nancy has given herself heart problems. She refuses to take anti-anxiety drugs, fearing if she ever has an autopsy, someone might find out and think she was addicted. Her uncontrolled emotions are wrecking her ability to think straight and eating her up physically as much as any cancer might do. Yet without acceptance she'll never know one single day of peace.

Over the years, I've shared the Serenity Prayer with Nancy many, many times:

God, grant me the serenity to accept the things I cannot change,
Courage to change the things I can,
And the wisdom to know the difference.

My heart breaks for people like Nancy. Oh, what a difference it would make in her life if only she could believe the truth of those words. If only she could accept the assurance of the Shepherd in the Twenty-third Psalm, who promised to never leave her or forsake her. Only then will she find peace. Only then will she find acceptance.

Chapter 6

IT'S ALL ABOUT TIME

—Dick

Throughout my life, I have used so many expressions using the word *time.*

What time is it? I don't have time. I do have time. Take your time. Time to go. If I have time. Remember the time when? Use your time wisely. We had the greatest time. So little time. The passing of time. I wish I had more time. Your time is up. Time sure flies!

As I wrote down these expressions, I came to realize just how significant they are now. They aren't just cute phrases. Most of the time I feel them, not hear them. I feel sad and panicky because of them. Ears play little part. The hammer, anvil, and stirrup need not exist. Thoughts and feelings about time now travel the sixteen-inches from my mind into my heart at light speed, then break it.

In this chapter, I want to express my thoughts and feelings regarding some of these expressions. Ironically, this is my longest chapter, and it took me the most time to write.

Time Sure Flies!

When Deb was diagnosed with cancer, I began to think about time more than usual. Even though Deb may outlive me, and I hope she does, cancer has become all about time and how quickly it passes. Time never pauses to eat. In fact, it tells me when I'm supposed to eat and when to stop. (I can take only one hour.) It wakes me up in the morning with an alarm and tells me to go to sleep at night. It tells me how long to stay at work and when my favorite shows come on television.

Most of the time, time is my boss, and I am subservient to it. I'm convinced the passage of time speeds up when you are over forty years old, along with the weight gain. I don't understand this phenomenon. Maybe I missed something during a time warp. Or maybe it has to do with the law of relativity. Surely Einstein understood it. Was he fat?

When I was a child, time seemed to last forever. In fact, I thought very little about it. I just played and played all day. When the sun came up, I played. I had a cousin I occasionally spent the night with. We loved playing together. I remember vividly when he would awaken me and say, "Get up! It's morning time!" That signaled another day of fun. Sunset was my only clue when it was time to quit playing, take my nightly bath, and go to bed.

When I was little, I hated the phrase "It's time to get up and go to school." All of a sudden, I became acutely aware of time. As an adult, I still feel a tinge of the same nausea when I hear a similar phrase: "It's time to get up and go to work."

That reminds me of a story. A man once told his wife he didn't want to get up and go to church. "I'm tired, and I don't like to be around people." She told him he had to get up. "You have to go! You're the preacher!"

I will probably cry as I write this chapter. But I hope my words convey what's in my heart. I'll probably pause many times to wipe my eyes as I struggle to see the computer monitor clearly. This is hard, but here goes.

Cancer and time are like strange bedfellows. I really can't think of one without the other. They do a song and dance for me every hour of every day. They can make me laugh or make me cry like a little baby, but usually the tears take the lead role. I have realized I both love and hate time at the same time, but the hate seems to take the lead role. I wonder if this is unusual.

On the one hand, I love time because it allows me to spend time with Deb. It has become more precious and valuable as we face an uncertain future. At one of our oncologist appointments, as the doctor reviewed her treatment regime, we heard a startling diagnosis. "Debbie, based on the size of the tumor and the staging (Stage IIIA), you have a 30 percent chance of recurrence." I remember he also used the term *mortality rate*. That sounded horrible! I had never heard that term used in the same sentence with Deb's name. Both statements sent chills down my spine.

"Damn! You've got to be kidding!" I cried in disbelief. (Yes, I know some people will be shocked at my language. Frankly, I don't care what they think.)

Up to that point, I was doing okay with all the news. I assumed there would be no problem with her complete healing, with very little chance of the cancer returning after all her surgeries and treatments. A 10 percent chance would have been too much, but 30 percent? That was unthinkable! That's almost one out of three! This was bad, very bad.

I tried to spin it in a positive light. "It could be worse. And 300 out of 1,000 sounds better, right?"

It was all about time.

Thirty-one years of marriage have already passed. Where did they go? What if we only have a few years left? Whatever the number of years we have left must be precious. I have to cherish them, protect them, and love them.

I try not to be negative and fatalistic. There are tens of thousands of women much younger than Deb who have faced breast cancer and lived to be old ladies. That, of course, is what we expect. I can't wait to see Deb when she's eighty. She'll still be wrinkle free, while I'm a shriveled-up old man. But she'll still be in love with me and I with her.

Cancer caused me to hate time too. I feel as if it may be robbing me of time, laughing at me as it packs its bag and heads for the door, carrying with it all future moments with Deb. How dare it? Who gave it permission to rip my heart out as it flies away with our time on its wings? I cannot let it get away. It must be caged and tamed like a wild animal.

Remember the Time When?

I am a very sentimental person. I will cry at the drop of a hat. Give me a memory, and I'll show you a grown man weeping like a baby. To me, nothing is more precious than good memories.

As I look around my home, everything I see is a memory. Carpet Deb picked out, dishes she bought, curtains she liked, shirts I hate, jewelry she wears, paint she chose, flowers she planted, pictures she kept, and thousands of things that fill a treasure chest of memories.

Even as I write, I'm wearing a shirt Deb got me for Christmas last year. I remember opening the present and telling her how much I loved it. In fact, I have never bought one stitch of clothing for myself. Deb has bought almost everything I wear.

There was a country song a few years ago called "The Song Remembers When." Everyone in love probably has a favorite song. I remember the time in 1978 when Deb and I were making out passionately (a.k.a. kissing) while the radio softly played LeBlanc and Carr's song, "Falling." I had just rounded first base and was on my way to second when Deb called me "out!" I argued with her, then she totally kicked me out of the game. That song peaked at number eleven on the Billboard Hot 100 while our love for each other topped at number one. Sounds corny, doesn't it? But Deb likes corny. Still today, whenever I hear that song, I remember when.

Our marriage hasn't always been fun all of the time. Our first year was really terrible. Marriage brings two people from other galaxies together. We were aliens. Strangers. Foreigners, each carrying our own suitcases stuffed full of differences that we began to unpack after we said, "I do."

If time flies when you're having fun, let's just say it also stopped many times that first year!

It took a while, but I can honestly say that after thirty years most of our old baggage has been opened and sifted through. Most of the items have been thrown away. We keep only one bag now, and it's much, much lighter. It's filled with memories.

We've also had tons of fun through the years. Trips to the mountains. Trips to the beach. Trips to Disney World. Telling jokes, laughing, and crying (sometimes that can be fun!) Making love, having our first child, having our second child, not having a third child. Dating, movies, dinner, just being together, doing stupid things, saying stupid things, and on and on. There are so many times when we have said, "We had the greatest time." Conversely, we've had to say, "We had the worst time" too. But as we reflect on some of them, those worst times have also been the best times. They made us laugh or made us stronger. Both results are good.

I have presided over many weddings over the years. I believe when many couples die and go to heaven, the first thing God will say to them is "I wish you had had more fun together."

I'm still looking forward to the best memories. I hope someday Deb and I will be sitting on a front porch, rocking back and forth with wrinkled old hands intertwined, saying, "Remember the time you *had* cancer?"

I Don't Have Time

As life screams by, things get so busy. Jobs, responsibilities, striving for success, making a living, selfishness—all take away time (or we let it). I've made so many promises and never followed-through. I've told my kids we would go camping, only later to say, "I don't have the time." I will take Deb on that cruise, *if I have the time.*

As I get older, this expression evolves into others. "I wish I had taken the time," or "Why didn't I take the time?" I've heard so many successful businessmen at the end of their lives say, "I wish I'd spent more time with my family and not at the office." As I look at my job, when I die someone will take my place in a week or so. I will eventually be long forgotten. Why don't I take the time sometimes? It is usually because I'm so busy making a living that I fail to make a life.

I'm a Baby Boomer. I'm a part of the generation born between 1946 and 1964. I was raised with an emphasis on getting a good education, followed by a good, stable job. This is not bad. But like many people my age, I have been programmed to think that life is defined by what I do for a living.

When men my age get together, usually one of the first questions asked is "What do you do?" or "Where do you work?" I've been asked that question many times, and I always answer by saying I'm a minister. As I look back, I wish I had said, "I'm a good husband and a great father. Oh, by the way, I have a job at—" My identity should be determined by what I am, rather than by what I do.

Where I work is important. It provides income, insurance, cars, home, food, clothing, fun, and vacations. But I have to understand it's just a means to an end. Now, the "end" needs to be taking care of Deb. That's my real job. I only work part-time for nine hours a day at the office. The other fifteen is what I do.

What do I do for a living? I'm a husband and a father. If I don't have the time to be that, I have failed miserably in life.

What Time Is It?

Cancer causes me to ask this particular question. I'm sure I looked at my watch while Deb was having her biopsy, but I don't remember the time. I had my watch on when the surgeon said the lumpectomy did not get all the cancer. My watch was still telling time when she had the double mastectomy, but I didn't notice. It still ticked away on my wrist during chemo, radiation, shots, sickness, nausea, aches and pains, and hundreds of other awful moments in time.

When it comes to cancer, my watch is ineffective. It cannot give me the correct time. Cancer has now become the timekeeper. It set the stop-watch at the moment of diagnosis. But it had already been traveling in the bloodstream, getting into lymph nodes, and forming tumors. It operated on its own schedule, as if following some kind of ghastly timed agenda.

The result of the lab report only communicated that Deb was on its agenda. Cancer will not share the specifics of the schedule it follows. How long had it been there? How long will it be there? When will it stop? When will we know if it is gone? Will it come back? And if it does, when?

I can only ask the questions, but so far all I hear is the incessant tick-tock of time screaming by.

The Bible teaches it is appointed unto each of us to die. That is surely encouraging and not very exciting! Every person I see will be dead one day. When? They don't know. When will I? Face it, I could have a heart attack or stroke as I write this next word.

How much longer will Deb live? With her type of cancer, is she closer to the end? If so, how close? If not, how long?

I wish I knew what time it is.

Many afternoons, Deb has sat alone in her favorite chaise ottoman with a West Point afghan covering her legs, our Chihuahua snuggled beneath it on her lap. Belle is the coldest and most needy dog in the universe. And, oh, did I mention totally useless? (Don't tell Deb I said that or she'll throw divorce papers at me. I truly believe Deb loves that dog more than me!)

To be honest, Belle has probably witnessed more of Deb's tears than I have. That little dog has been such a comfort to Deb when no one else is around. She has told me many times how Belle has climbed up and licked away her tears. Of course, then I'd say something stupid like, "Belle must've been really thirsty." I wish Chihuahuas could talk. Or maybe I don't. I'm not sure my heart could stand it.

One of the most difficult times for Deb is always the most difficult time for me. These are the evenings at home when everything seems to be going well at first. We may be laughing at a television show or listening intently to the latest from the political grapevine on our favorite cable news network.

I should tell you that Deb is a political news ... loves keeping up with what's going on in the ... could do a much better job at running our coun... White House. She's not only a frustrated docto... cian as well.

All of a sudden it hits. I can tell before it h... happen. She becomes very quiet. She begins to slowly panic and start crying. Her voice quivers, and she literally begins to shake. Anxiety takes over. She begins to sob uncontrollably. I run over to hold her.

"Dick, I'm so scared I'm going to die! Deep in my bones, I feel that my cancer is going to come back, and I'm so scared!" Every ache and pain becomes another symptom of cancer. She knows too much.

Then part of her tears carry a heartbreaking message to me, "I don't want to leave you." That's perhaps the hardest sentence for me to hear. My heart aches so deeply when these six words invade my mind.

I find it so very easy to dwell on statements like this. They camp out in my brain and never leave. They build bonfires and dance around my mind like crazed cannibals, nibbling away at my sanity. I wish I could just flush my brain like a toilet to rid it of such terrible thoughts. Just the idea of being separated from Deb causes me to panic. I can't imagine it. She has been by my side for more than three decades. I've been married to her longer than I was single.

But here's the rub. Deb knows how much I would miss her. She knows she is my very life. She knows how living without her could affect me. She literally fears for me if she should die first.

I never want to discuss this possibility. Yes, I have heard of the Queen of Denial. I am the King. But she needs to talk with me about the possibility of her dying before me. It is so hard for me to do that. I stumble and stutter. I can barely look her in the eyes when she talks about it. But she makes me. She looks straight in my eyes and says, "If I die before you, I want you to promise me that you will be okay . . . that you won't do anything to yourself." I say, "Oh, that will never happen. I'll probably die before you anyway. Let's just don't talk about it."

That is not what she needs to hear, so she tries a second or third time. She gets in my face again and says, "I want to hear you make me this promise, that you will be okay and that you won't do anything to yourself." With tears flowing down my cheeks, I know what she needs me to say: "Honey, I promise, I will be okay, and I won't do anything to myself." God forbid if that should ever happen, I must and will keep my promise.

nights, Deb has vivid dreams. They aren't nightmares that
her wake up screaming, although they do cause fear and anxiety
en she remembers them. Usually they are about being separated
from me or the family. Dreams about separation come often. I assure
her these dreams are not prophetic and have nothing to do with pre-
dicting the future. But they're still disturbing—to both of us.

My heart breaks whenever she has these experiences. I can't do
anything but hold her and attempt to comfort and console her. I have
to reassure her everything is going to be okay. I give her an anxiety
pill. I've taken some myself. I wipe my eyes. It is so very hard.

After she has relaxed, I tell her I'm going to the store to pick up
something we need. But it's just an excuse to get out of the house so I
can bawl my eyes out. While I'm gone, I call my sisters and cry as I tell
them what happened and how much it hurts me to see Deb like that. I
feel like I can't keep it together. They understand and try to reassure
me. And it does help me. Of course, Deb has caught on to this. When
I get back she asks, "You called your sisters, didn't you?"

I'm not a good liar.

Then I wonder if she's right. Will her cancer come back? Do the
dreams mean something? Are the pains here and there indicative of a
recurrence? I feel so helpless . . . and sometimes hopeless.

What time is it?

One night I was lying in bed looking at her face as she slept
soundly. She was lying on her back and looked so peaceful. A haunting thought washed over me. I wondered what it would be like to never
see her face again. I had to get up and leave the room. The grief was
unbearable as I wrestled with the hypothetical thought.

When I conclude talking with someone about Deb's cancer, many
times I'll say, "Well, we just take it one day at a time." Part of that is
true, I guess. Or at least it sounds good. Yes, Deb and I should take
each day as a gift. We should seize the moment. But in all reality, that
sentence is a lie. With the possible and devastating effects of Deb's
cancer ever looming, there is no way I can take it one day at a time.
How can I possibly look at her without thinking, "What if I lose her tomorrow, or the next day, or next year?" Those fears are so engrained in
my "one day at a time" that it's impossible to stay in the moment.

Deb and I are honored to be writing this book. We certainly hope
and pray our story will be helpful to others. But in the process of
writing our book, something hit me like a ton of bricks. I remember

contacting my sisters and our co-writer Diane Moody with my concern. The manuscript deadline seemed doable. This would be necessary in order for the book to be ready for the publication date. I was so excited to think the book could be out that month. But right after I heard the date, and I mean immediately after, I realized—with Deb's cancer, there was a 30 percent possibility a recurrence might occur before then. *She could be dead before the book even comes out.*

What if that happened? It wasn't about a book deadline; it was about Deb. It scared me to think for some unknown reason her cancer had her on a deadline.

What time is it?

Take Your Time

I get it. Taking your time normally means to be patient, don't be in a hurry, and so on. A person can usually do his best work when not rushing to get a job done. This is the exact opposite of me. I am Type A, hyper, nervous, and neurotic. I am always early for meetings. I am always in a hurry. I walk fast, talk fast, eat fast, and think fast. When I go by my secretary's cubicle, I create such a breeze that papers fly off her desk. I go to movies an hour before they start to avoid lines.

But when taking your time relates to Deb's cancer, I shout a resounding NO! This is not an option! Cancer runs too fast. It can win a marathon in record time. I can't keep up with it.

How can you take your time when the tumor can grow larger with each passing day or rush to spread elsewhere in the body? Treatment must be *now*. Surgery must be quick.

In a later chapter, Deb elaborates on a very scary episode about dizziness. Once, while getting out of bed, she passed out and fell on the floor. We were terrified. Being schooled in oncology, she immediately thought her cancer had metastasized in the brain as this is one of the primary symptoms. There was no "take your time" to see if it would go away. She called her doctor and had an MRI done that next day. Thankfully it turned out to be only an inner-ear problem.

A few weeks later, I received an e-mail response from a friend of mine whose wife had breast cancer. After her treatment and surgery, she was doing great. She was in her second year after she had ended her treatments. I had e-mailed him to let him know I was thinking about him and his wife and was happy to hear how well she was doing. He replied that she had begun having lower back pain. Her cancer had returned with a vengeance, metastasizing in the liver and bones. He told me with much regret that if Deb ever started to have lower back pain, to immediately contact the doctor. They had waited because they thought it was just a herniated disk.

Later, Deb did start to have lower back pain. I didn't have to tell her about the e-mail warning from my friend. She already knew what it could mean. She got checked immediately and was relieved to know her cancer had not spread.

We decided not to take our time when the MRI of her right breast had shown some spots the doctor said were nothing to worry about. They would keep an eye on it. We decided not to wait to see what might become of it.

There Is So Little Time

My life is like a vapor. Yes, that is from the Bible. I am here one day and gone the next. Once it seemed like I was running ahead of time. Now it's passing me by much too quickly, and I'm trying to catch up with it. It will not pause and pass the baton back to me. There is no back button or undo icon.

In a seminary class, we were handed a blank death certificate as part of a class assignment. I had to fake my death. I had to think about the year when I died, where I died, how I died, my survivors, and so forth. I didn't really take it seriously, nor did the rest of my class. Still, there was something ominous and telling about it.

I wanted to die a very old man in my sleep at night. I would be survived by my wife, kids, grandchildren, and great-great grandchildren. I wanted to die in the mountains where I would have a beautiful view, though I don't remember which mountain range I wrote down. But I wanted to die while it was raining with an outside temperature of around forty degrees. I wanted sore-throat weather. Miserable. Not cold enough to snow, just miserable. I wanted it rainy, wet, dark and dreary . . . like an Edgar Allen Poe story. A raven standing nearby would be perfect.

Why did I fill it out that way? When I think back on it, I wonder, was I some sort of weird maniac? I probably did it because I fear death. The dark dreariness was likely a good indication of my fear. I would think most folk fear death too. But the wet and rainy thing—what did that mean? I want people to remember me, to be affected by my death. What better way to remember my death than to have a terrible sore throat: *Yes, I remember Dick Church. That's when I had the worst sore throat of my life.*

Of course, what I'm really saying is I hope my life has significance and people will miss me when I'm gone. Like most people, I strive for meaning and significance. We all want to believe we're here for a purpose. We all want to find a reason for life.

I've heard that it's not as important how I arrived in this world as how I leave. Did my life make a difference? Is the world a better place because I passed through it? Life is so brief. I want to finish it well. Whether or not I have cancer, I am moving through the seasons of my life. My spring and summer have already passed. I am well into the late autumn and on the verge of winter. I can feel the cold winds blow from time to time.

When October rolls around, Deb and I always drive to the mountains. Sometimes the autumn colors are so overwhelmingly beautiful it takes our breath away. I've been told the striking colors are caused when a certain amount of rain has fallen during the summer months, making the leaves hold onto the trees a while longer. Some scientist may correct me, but I'm not going to check this out. I'm not writing a hydrological thesis here. But something causes these extraordinary colors.

Other times we've visited the mountains during October only to find the leaves nowhere near as pretty. Most had just turned brown. I'm guessing the reverse must be true, meaning little rain must have fallen during those summers.

Deb is the most important person in my life. I realize how very lucky I am to have been married to her for more than thirty years. Now, because of her cancer, the leaves of our life are not as pretty as they once were. But we hope that next October they will be beautiful once again. Whether cancer is involved or not, the reality is that one day the leaves will fall. Life only gives us a limited number of Octobers anyway. So it's imperative that Deb and I take as many drives as we can.

There is so little time in life.

Use Your Time Wisely

Recently I calculated something I found shocking. Living in Atlanta is akin to living in your car. Traffic is horrendous, and it takes so much time to get anywhere. It seems as if it takes an hour to go to the bathroom. I spend twelve hours a week commuting back and forth to work. When multiplied over a year, I spend twenty-six full twenty-four-hour days in the car just driving to and from work! That's almost a month each year spent sitting in my car!

If I had that time with Deb, it would be equivalent to another day and a half of vacation each week!

But at least I have a job, right?

Figure it another way. My round-trip commute is seventy-eight miles per day. Multiply that by 260 workdays and that equals 20,280 miles per year. Now, multiply that by nine years, which is how long I've been at my present job. That totals 182,520 miles. The earth's circumference at the equator is about 25,000 miles. Divide that into 182,520, and I have circled the globe 7.3 times on my commute.

Stop the analogies. I am so depressed.

When Deb was diagnosed, one of the first thoughts to cross my mind was: Are we going to grow old together? I had never thought about that before. I had no reason to. Most healthy people don't think about their own mortality. But there it was, like an unwelcome visitor knocking at my door.

Over the months, I began to really examine my life as her husband. So many wonderful memories created over the thirty years of our marriage. But then it came, bringing along with it sadness and tears. It was but one word: *Regret.*

That is such a horrible word. All the "If I had only—" or "I should have—" or "Why didn't I—?" statements and questions have become a part of my daily mental routine.

I have asked Deb so many times during her bout with cancer, "Have I been a good husband? Would you do it all over again?" "Yes," she will say. "You're the best husband in the world." She always answers yes to these questions. But deep down inside, I feel so guilty. I know so many flaws and failures in me. I want to tell her I'm sorry. And I have. Sorry for what?

There is so much I regret. I wish I could go back and change many things. Some seem so silly and stupid. But the most seemingly silly and stupid things can be what you regret the most. I wish I had:

- taken her dancing;
- not gotten so angry at the traffic;

- paid more attention when she talked;
- fed the babies more (did I ever do that?) in the middle of the night;
- not been so serious;
- held her hand more;
- told her I loved her more;
- been kinder, gentler, and more forgiving.

The list is not exhaustive. But I must remember it's not too late to shorten lists like this.

Cancer has caused me to reevaluate how I use my time. The most important question in the world must be: Did I use my time wisely? In the movie *Dead Poets Society,* Robin Williams' character teaches his students the term *carpe diem*: seize the day. I'm trying to learn how to take advantage of every moment I have with Deb. I fail so many times and doze off.

No more regrets. That would feel so good.

It's All About Time

I am so happy there are many breast cancer awareness walks and promotional items such as commercials and billboards. They are so important to keep the public aware of this terrible disease and to encourage people to give money for research. I am praying researchers will find a cure and soon. But I must confess something. I get very uncomfortable when Deb and I are watching TV together and one of these commercials comes on. I act like I don't see it. I think Deb does the same thing. There's no conversation. We make no remarks about it, give no high-fives or cheers. If I ignore it, cancer will go away.

October is Breast Cancer Awareness month. I see pink ribbons everywhere. I see bumper stickers that say Save the TaTas. Even the NFL players wear pink shoes or sweat bands. I see people in pink shirts dart in and out of stores at the mall and in restaurants. Both young and old display their concern and hope for a cure.

I wonder how many of these people have friends or relatives who have cancer. Or do they have it? Are they in remission? I wonder how many of them had someone they knew and loved who died of cancer. But pink? Right now for me, it's just a colorful clock. A pink timepiece that never goes backward. As it relates to cancer, I'm praying someone will soon find a way to break it into a thousand pieces. And I hope Deb and a million more survivors will be there to see it—when the only purpose of a pink ribbon is to adorn a little girl's hair.

In Ecclesiastes 3:1-8, the author writes:

There is a time for everything,
and a season for every activity under heaven:
a time to be born and a time to die,
a time to plant and a time to uproot,
a time to kill and a time to heal,
a time to tear down and a time to build,
a time to weep and a time to laugh,
a time to mourn and a time to dance,
a time to scatter stones and a time to gather them,
a time to embrace and a time to refrain,
a time to search and a time to give up,
a time to keep and a time to throw away,
a time to tear and a time to mend,
a time to be silent and a time to speak,
a time to love and a time to hate,
a time for war and a time for peace.

Life is all about time and what I do with it. But just as there is a time to be born, there is a time to die. How do I live in between?

While I have performed many weddings, I have also presided over many funerals. Somewhere in my remarks, I usually refer to a tombstone where it shows the date when the person was born and the date of their passing. "In between is a dash. Life is all about the dash. That is where we live, learn, and love."

Deb and I face her horrible disease; tomorrow remains forever unknown. My tomorrow is unknown as well. All we have right now is the dash. It is what we will do in the dash that counts.

Chapter 7

IN SICKNESS AND IN HEALTH

—Deb

Debbie and Dicky sitting in a tree, K-i-s-s-i-n-g.
First comes love, then comes marriage,
then comes Debbie with a baby carriage.

For many years, my view of marriage could be summed up with that simple limerick. All I needed was someone to fall in love with and marry. As a hopeless romantic, I believed marriage was easy. After all, I watched every episode of the *Donna Reed Show* and *Father Knows Best*. While I watched them, I wondered what in the world could be hard about it?

Married to a pediatrician, Donna Reed always wore a beautiful dress, pearl necklace, earrings, and high heels while she cleaned house. By the end of the day, she had done all the laundry, vacuumed every square inch of floor, cooked a delicious and healthy meal, solved all her neighbors' problems over coffee, made cookies for her two children, and greeted her husband at the door with a big kiss. Actually, it was only a peck. Had it been a long, romantic French kiss, the show would have been taken off the air. That would have been considered porn back then.

In *Father Knows Best*, father Jim Anderson, played by Robert Young, always had the right answer for his three children. He smoked a pipe and usually lounged around the house in a suit and tie. Occasionally he dressed in wool sweater. Most of the problems in the home involved youngest daughter "Kitten's" occasional white lie, teenage son, Bud, not coming home on time, what dress Betty would wear to the prom, and assorted dating dilemmas. Dad smiled constantly. But I imagine if he had to deal with drugs, alcohol, sex, and abortion issues with his children, he would have smiled less.

His marriage was never in trouble. It began with a quick kiss in the morning (see above) as he left for work. His wife, Margaret, whom he always called "dear," didn't work outside the home, of course. It also seemed as if she didn't do very much work inside the home either. The beds made themselves, and the home stayed spotless and neat.

Then, upon his return home from slaving away at work, the day ended with a quick kiss (see above) goodnight as they each made their way to their own twin bed. How they had children remains a mystery to me. If this is marriage, then it didn't seem too difficult. I loved my twin bed. A piece of cake, I thought.

Every episode ended with self-esteem intact, good morals upheld, happiness maintained, problems solved, and an ever-increasing love for each member of the family.

It seemed to me that every problem in a marriage, or life, for that matter, could be solved with a simple kiss between husband and wife. I was honestly that naïve. But I have learned after more than thirty years of marriage that passionately making out with my husband or even prolonged sex with him can't solve every problem. Though he's had fun trying! He loves "solving" problems.

Dick and I were married on December 30, 1978. He mentioned previously in chapter 4 how we met in seminary, our first date, and how we fell in love. I will trust his version of this story, knowing full well it's slanted somewhat to make him look better.

We had a beautiful church wedding. It was a big church wedding. It was an expensive church wedding! Looking back, we have wished so many times we hadn't spent so much money on our wedding. We would have used it to buy food or make a car payment.

Dick was a real pain in the you-know-what as we made plans for our wedding. Like most girls, I'd dreamed about my wedding day my entire life. A Prince Charming would ride up on a white horse and carry me away to a beautiful castle where I would live in rich extravagance happily ever after.

But my Prince Charming turned out to be a broke seminary student driving up on a used motorcycle. His "castle" was a bedroom leased for $40 a month from a retired missionary to China. The only extravagance he possessed was a crusty crock pot and the sheets on his bed (which he never changed, by the way).

Yes, Dick could be a real pain. He argued with me over what to wear at the wedding, the decorations, what china to buy, the number of bridesmaids needed, the music and songs to be played, the singer who sang the songs, and the food to be served at the reception. I know you're surprised by these revelations. He would never mention such matters in his chapters! He wants you to think he's perfect. Not! But now it's my turn. Payback time!

No, not really. He is the most wonderful husband in the world, even though he has his moments.

It may sound like we hated each other right before the wedding, but it went off without a hitch. As did the reception. But something churned inside me when we left for our honeymoon. I plastered on a smile as we drive off in our car painted in multicolored wedding graffiti.

I was frightened and unsure. What had I done? Did I make the right decision?

We honeymooned in Florida and Mexico. My dad paid for it. Prince Charming was broke, remember? I recall lying in the bed of our hotel suite while Dick made strange and unusual sounds in the bathroom. Come to think of it, I'd never heard particular sounds like that before.

I felt confused and unhappy. I tried to hide my feelings from Dick, but my efforts were unsuccessful. It wasn't that I didn't love him—I did. Desperately! I wanted more than anything to be happy, but I felt as if I couldn't be honest with him about my fears.

After a couple of nights in Miami, we flew to Club Med in Cancun, Mexico. Stop and think about that for a moment. Two "godly" seminary students arriving on Fornication Beach for singles, lounge chairs filled with topless beauties surrounded by gazing, drooling, and groping men. Dick promised me he was not among those drooling. At least I never saw him drooling. I decided to wear an overcoat on the beach to keep any eyes off me, just in case some guy had a thing for one-piece bathing suits.

Our travel agent made a huge mistake in recommending this place. She based it on Dick's love of scuba diving. The ocean was clear. But we had no clue prior to our arrival that we would be eating dinner with a dozen tequila-drunken, hedonistic singles sitting around the same table. We expected to be alone and dine by romantic candlelight each night. But that's not Club Med. We can laugh about it now. Really.

The second night, Montezuma's revenge attacked me with full force. We both quickly learned what "in sickness and in health" truly means. We just didn't know how gross it would be. Eventually, it visited Dick, and we waited on each other, depending on who felt better at the moment. I must have missed the diarrhea episode on the *Donna Reed Show*. A sad realization came to me: This is what marriage is—two people in love living together, with all the ups and downs (including bending over the commode) of life.

I didn't want to believe this is all there was to it. I was still looking for the castle!

We returned from Mexico and faced truly hard days with schoolwork, finishing seminary, bills, laundry . . . and the most difficult issue of all, my in-laws.

When I married Dick, he married my family and I married his. At first, dealing with my in-laws proved to be the greatest challenge for me. Their mistakes and misconceptions about me and my mistakes and misconceptions about them collided head-on. Dick, as the baby of his family, had been protected. They thought he was perfect. Now *this woman* had taken him away.

While "taking him away" was never my intention, their perception of it caused problems for us. For years. So much tension mounted on our trips to visit his family that I literally had to stop and throw up before we arrived. It was that bad for me. Only after many years, I mean many years, has a loving relationship been forged between his family and me. It took work from both sides, but now I can truly call my in-laws my family. And it is wonderful!

Days stretched into months, and months stretched into years as we tiptoed our way through life. Easy days and hard ones came and went, but we were basically happy.

Dick had a tendency to want to move a lot. He was searching, trying to decide what he wanted to be when he grew up. Seminary had confused him both theologically and practically. There was a huge disconnect between his liberal graduate-school education and his conservative Christian background. Frankly, he didn't know what to believe anymore.

We moved to Florida on a whim to be near some very good friends. We had no jobs and very little money, but we made it. It was exciting! Over the next three years, Dick eventually came to a point where he could use aspects of his liberal theological education within a conservative church. He became the minister of education at First Baptist Church of Indian Rocks in Largo. We loved the friends we made in that big three-thousand-member church.

While there, we added two children to our family. As Dick told you, I had a rough time getting pregnant at first. I had two painful miscarriages before our son, Richard Scott, was born. Then three years later I almost died after giving birth to our beautiful daughter, Mary Elizabeth.

Raising babies put an enormous strain on our marriage. Dick was gone many evenings on church-related work, such as visitation, so I was left alone to care for the kids. It was especially hard when the kids were sick. With him gone so much, I never had a break. Also, we never seemed to have enough money because we decided early on that I should stay home with the children until they started school. I loved being home with them but always worried about balancing the budget. Most reverends don't make a lot of money.

As I mentioned in chapter 3, we moved from our church in Largo to a larger church in Fort Lauderdale. It was not the Camelot experience he had hoped for. Then it was off to Tennessee, then back to Clearwater, Florida. While in Clearwater, I began working in oncology. And I loved it.

Why we then moved to Powder Springs, Georgia, is difficult to determine. *Oh no,* I thought. *Another big mistake.* I didn't want to leave Florida! Primarily, I think Dick wanted to be closer to his mother and sick father who lived in North Carolina. An even larger church wanted him, so he accepted the offer. As it turned out, the move enabled us to be nearer to my parents as well. Within just four short years, all four of our parents died.

These moves not only affected me, they affected our children as well. Starting over in new schools, new churches, and having to constantly make new friends all took a toll on our kids. I have to be honest; I held some animosity toward Dick. I didn't like being uprooted over and over while he tried to find what he was looking for, only to be disappointed time and again. His disappointments were mine too. I felt an added pressure to keep our home happy and content. Many times I succeeded, but often I failed. Remarkably, Scott and Mary have done very well, and I am so proud of them.

When we moved to Georgia, I continued working in the field of oncology and enjoyed every minute of it.

After a few years of ministry at the new church, Dick left to join the team of the largest mission agency in the world, headquartered here in the Atlanta area. He has been employed there for almost ten years. It felt good to finally settle down, although Powder Springs is still not what I would consider Camelot!

Even though we've had the challenges of career moves, house moves, and disappointments, we remain very much in love. Like other couples, we've faced thousands of other little issues that arise in marriage, some having the potential to destroy them, but we've survived.

But by far, and I mean by far, the greatest challenge in our lives is cancer. As I said before, I know all about cancer. I've studied it for years and counseled thousands of patients. Some have survived for dozens of years and are considered cured. Others passed away only days after diagnosis. I have seen it all. But in every case I have learned as much from them as they have from me. It's difficult to explain. When I counsel them, they counsel me.

"Jim" and "Betty" came to me for counseling. Both successful in their careers, they are witty and charming, a fun couple to be around. But Betty has Stage IV breast cancer with metastasis to her bones. For more than eight years she has received successful treatment for this disease. She is a continual inspiration to all of us. She dresses for every chemotherapy, determined to look her best. While she sits in the infusion area receiving treatment, she encourages others. She has seen others come and go, but her determination and courage keep her going.

However, after a few years she came to me crying. On the outside everything looked fine. But on the inside she was nervous. She thought about life and death and was trying desperately to live each day to the fullest. She went out for lunch with friends, she traveled, and she didn't wear a watch. The definition of time had changed for her, and she didn't want to be constricted by it.

But her husband didn't understand this dynamic. They were not communicating. Their intimate life had changed, and he didn't seem to have the same urgency for living each day to the fullest. She felt cheated. "Why doesn't he get it? I may have a few months to live or twenty years. But I want him to be present with me *now*. He plans and plans for the future. He doesn't plan for now. I want him to plan for now!"

I guess we are all guilty of this phenomenon: When I graduate, when I get married, when we have children, when we buy a house with a white picket fence. All of these are euphemisms that project happiness to sometime in the future.

Thus began our long journey together, the husband and wife reviewing with the counselor their important life decisions, along with their communication problems. We were in different countries and had begun to speak different languages, neither understanding the other. We had to go through the process of learning a new common language so we could interpret what the other was saying. We had to listen with ears that understood what the other one needed. This endeavor sounds very easy, but it truly takes many hours; just as it took many hours to learn to speak and understand primary language.

Jim and Betty's intimacy had been imperiled, and their communication had broken down so severely that their sex life was nonexistent. Now I have never claimed to be a sex therapist. But in marriage, especially those marriages touched by cancer, intimacy can be greatly damaged. Cancer touches every aspect of life, so of course it can affect sexual expression as well. We went back to the very basics.

Jim and Betty are very lucky. They wanted to save their marriage, and they worked very hard. They loved each other, and their love was the starting point we always came back to.

I have seen far too many cases with the opposite outcome. Once a man came to me and actually stated: "I am no longer attracted to my wife. I didn't sign up for this, so I am leaving. I know you think I am awful, but I have to consider my needs. I'm only thirty-nine years old. Y'know what I mean?"

I remember specifically at that moment thinking I would hit him. I did express my dissatisfaction with him quite forcefully, and it took every ounce of restraint not to slap him across his face. Fortunately he left quickly.

Another man told his wife, "You're hideous to look at. I've already begun seeing someone else." He told her this just a few weeks after her diagnosis. "I'm leaving you the house and the dog, but I'm moving on." Apparently his time could not be wasted on such trivia.

Then there was "Shelly," an advanced breast-cancer patient who was unique because she had to go through almost a year of treatment. Her husband, a local law enforcement agent, would come with her to treatments, but he was not at all loving and kind with her. During one of my one-on-one sessions with Shelly, she asked if I would see them together and observe them, then advise them on their marriage.

While I don't profess to be a marriage counselor, I recognize the strains of cancer on a marriage, so I agreed. "Rob" came in, very aloof, but obviously interested in his wife's care. He seemed to want to understand what his wife was going through and what the treatments were doing to her body.

She turned to him. "But you don't act interested when you're at home."

I asked him, "Rob, why is that?"

"I don't know how to take care of her. Maybe you can make some suggestions."

From the beginning, I'd had an uneasy feeling about him. I didn't feel that he was being honest with himself or with Shelly. In a psychosocial assessment, knowing that he was a police officer, I thought he might just be a little rough around the edges and not sure how to express his emotions and concern. Maybe his day-to-day job interfered with his ability to cope at home. Often people in law enforcement have a difficult time with that transition.

Eventually he stopped coming to her chemotherapy treatments. He stopped coming to our counseling sessions. Shelly told me things were getting much worse at home. As she faced her upcoming double mastectomy, her elderly parents made the trip from North Carolina to be with her during her surgery and afterward to help take care of her. I was alarmed by how frail both her mother and father were when I met them in the hospital, knowing it would be difficult for them to physically care for their daughter after her surgery.

The day of Shelly's surgery, Rob was not at the hospital. Her parents were very angry with him. The dysfunctional dynamics of this family were worse than I'd known. But I had a gut feeling that the husband was not being faithful to his wife. Eventually, toward the end of her surgery, he showed up. He acted concerned and hugged Shelly's parents, who accepted the gesture because they obviously needed his support.

A couple of months later Shelly came to see me. Her husband had asked her to go on a cruise, and she was so excited. We talked about how much that meant to her and about their plans to discuss the possibility of reconstructive surgery. She felt that their marriage was turning a new page and had wonderful hopes for their future.

On the last night of the cruise, Rob broke up with Shelly. He told her she was one of the ugliest women he'd ever seen, and since the mastectomy he'd realized he never wanted to be with her again. He couldn't stand being in her presence, much less have any kind of sexual attraction to her. He explained the cruise as a "kind" way to tell her he was leaving her.

Immediately upon their return, he moved out and admitted he'd been seeing someone else throughout the entire time she'd been battling cancer. He told her the other woman had encouraged him to take her on the cruise to break up with her. Shelly was devastated. When she came to see me and told me what had happened, I was so angry with Rob.

Unfortunately, it reminded me of how important it was to accept my initial gut reaction because it was usually right. I hadn't liked Rob from the beginning and questioned his sincerity. As it turned out, from the very beginning he'd had no intention whatsoever of staying with Shelly.

In Georgia, a divorce can be finalized in as little as thirty days if it's not contested, so the divorce was quickly over. The day she saw her marriage officially dissolved, Shelly returned home to find that her dog had died. She called me late that afternoon, hysterical. I saw her the next morning and tried to help her through her grief.

This is a story I saw time and time again. The exact circumstances changed, but the story was the same. A lot of men, especially younger men, would leave their wives after breast cancer. They never gave a good reason, though most of them never spoke to me directly after they left.

But time and again, I could see it coming. The husband would stop coming to treatment with his wife, stop coming to our counseling sessions, stop taking care of her at home, stop showing any kind of compassion or concern, and then he would leave.

It happened so frequently that Dr. Bruce Gould, an oncologist at Northwest Georgia Oncology, stopped me in the hallway one day and asked me, "Debbie, is there any kind of documentation about the correlation between breast cancer and divorce? Why do husbands leave their wives when they have breast cancer?"

I had no answer for him, except that I'd seen the pattern over and over. Is it a sexual turn-off for the husband? Did the husband simply not take his wedding vow seriously enough to be there in sickness and in health? Or is it just the fact that cancer always exacerbates whatever type of relational dynamics are already in place in a marriage?

When cancer happens, it's like a bomb goes off in the middle of that relationship. If you were fighting before, the fighting will get worse. If finances were tough before, they're worse now. If you argued about the kids, you'll argue even more now.

But the opposite also happens. I've seen wives who were miserable in their marriages, and when that cancer bomb goes off, they begin to realize how precious life is. "My life is too valuable to put up with this. I'm out of here!"

While I never condone divorce, I would never tell a patient, "No, you have to stay in a miserable situation. You have to just put up with all that emotional abuse." I cannot tell them that. I simply tell them they have to do what they have to do. If there is physical abuse, I am required legally to encourage separation.

My heart and soul hurt for all these individuals. You probably believe I'm making these stories up, but they have happened and continue to happen. Has our society ingrained individuals with such selfishness and depravity of soul that they have no feelings of responsibility for others? Is it the lack of God in their lives?

I don't know the answers to these questions, but I have always felt honored to stand in the gap for these individuals. To take them by the hand and help them through their journey of cancer. They have shown me such strength and courage, even through their tears.

I am the lucky one. I have a husband and family who have stood by me from the very beginning. My honey-do list is still there on the refrigerator door. But even if those items don't get done, I know my husband loves me desperately and will support me forever.

And this is the love God intended couples to have.

On the first night of our honeymoon, Dick read a poem he'd written for me. It says:

I dream of a home, beneath the mountains,
　in a valley lost in their fold,
Beside the sound of rolling rivers, flowing wild and free.
But my desires seem far away, lost in the beauty of your eyes.
For wherever there is you and me, there is home.

Early in this chapter, I told you about the sad realization that came to me while we were on our honeymoon in Cancun: that marriage is two people in love living together, with the ups and downs (and yes, even including bending over the commode) of life. I didn't want to believe that this was all there was to it.

But after thirty years of marriage, I have discovered this: It is two people in love with each other, living together. It has its ups and downs. Yes, even cancer. And sometimes I still don't want to believe it. But you know what? Whether sick or healthy, rich or poor, during good times or bad . . . with Dick, I have found Camelot after all.

Chapter 8

HAVE MERCY ON ME!

—Dick

An *interesting* chapter to write! But sex is always interesting for a man, right?

When I told Deb I was beginning to work on this chapter, she asked, "Why?" We laughed, and then she quipped, "Shouldn't take you a long time to do." We both agreed. After a short dialogue we decided this chapter only needed one page with one word: "None." That way, it would be very simple to translate into hundreds of languages. When it comes to sex, every culture must have the word *none* in its vocabulary.

I was thirty-three when my dad told me about the birds and the bees . . . not hardly. Honestly, I don't think he ever had this discussion with me. If memory serves me well, I came to learn about this stuff in elementary school. It was about the same time I found out Santa Claus wasn't real. Maybe it was Santa who told me about the birds and the bees!

I went to a very raw elementary school full of characters. The best schools were on the other side of the tracks. They had names like Beverly Hills and MacAlister. I went to Long School. Plain and boring Long School. Known as the poor people's school, Long was within walking distance of my house. An absurdly high fence surrounded the entire school property, making it appear prison-like. Gates with chained padlocks kept students in and out.

In the first grade I recall little Andy sitting behind me, little Becky in front of me, and Bubba beside me. I thought Bubba was so cool because he could drive himself to school. He had just turned sixteen. I think this was his ninth attempt to pass the first grade. Okay, not really, but some inmates seemed so much more mature than me, both mentally and physically. I would not have been surprised if little Andy smoked cigars, Becky dipped snuff, and Bubba was married.

Most kids in my school were rednecks and rough necks. I guess, by default, I was too. Fights broke out at recess as routinely as kickball and playing marbles. Some kids cussed. Empty Pabst Blue Ribbon cans accumulated under the monkey bars. Anchors and Mom tattoos appeared on thin forearms, and teachers often sent Lisa home for wearing mini miniskirts. She was seven at the time. The boys protested her dismissals as unfair. Bubba lead a revolt.

But I exaggerate . . . just a little.

The birds and bees discussion was nothing new. It was part of the playground curriculum, and every playground had one or two experts on the subject. Throngs of giggling boys flocked to them like they were charismatic cult leaders. I think I saw Becky there once too. They had magazine pictures to use as references. They provided footnotes and bibliographies for further reading assignments. Although there were a few errors and some fill in the blanks, most of the information shared was correct.

As Deb mentioned in another chapter, one of her patients used a very apropos phrase to describe the sexual escapades of a man whose wife has cancer. It's called mercy sex. She understood that her husband still had needs, even if she didn't.

Mercy sex. Now that is an erotic phrase. I can just picture walking down the back streets of Amsterdam and seeing the words *Mercy Sex for Sale* blinking a red neon invitation. Bouncers probably require entrance fees and an oncologist-approved MRI. In Amsterdam it might be a multimillion dollar enterprise.

When guys get together, the subject of sex always seems to come up at some point in the conversation. I think there are three parts of a man's brain: the conscious, sub-conscious, and sex. I've read in survival books that a man can live without food for up to two weeks. He can live without water for three to four days. But he can't live a day without sex. Well, maybe two days.

I'm sure Deb will try to edit this chapter for me—if she reads it at all. She'll be embarrassed by my quips. I'm sure she'll ask the editors to delete the entire chapter.

The older a man gets, well, the older he gets. Age affects every part of the body. Now, you know where I could go with this, but I will spare you the millions of jokes. (If you have some new ones, let me know.) And I'm sorry ladies, but you get old too.

Deb and I used to lead many marriage conferences. We discussed topics such as the importance of communication, conflict resolution, and how to handle money. Also on the agenda: sex. (I probably put it there.)

During those particular sessions we would break up into two groups. Deb took the ladies, and I took the men to another room. In the guys' room we would laugh and give each other high fives. We could have kept talking the rest of the day. We watched DVDs and shared endless jokes. Once we rewrote the preamble to Constitution: Man is endowed by his Creator with certain unalienable rights, and among them is life, liberty, and the pursuit of sex. John Adams must have rolled over in his grave.

I always wondered why the ladies' session took less than five minutes.

In one of our conferences we didn't break up into two groups. Both sexes remained in the same room. We had an archaic overhead projector that only worked part of the time and a stack of various slides. The slides had only words, no pictures. Deb would have left the room if pictures were included. I always thought about throwing a picture or two up on the screen just for fun. I did subscribe to *Sports Illustrated* once. Come to think of it, we should have planned all our conferences during the summer to coincide with the swimsuit edition.

During one of these "plenary sessions," Deb made the biggest faux pas of her life. I talked first, sharing about the importance of sex for men. It took four hours. When it was Deb's turn, she closed in prayer. Just kidding.

Deb talked about the woman's perspective on sex, mentioning the importance of things like caring, loving, sweetness, tenderness, giving, holding hands, and gentleness from men as all part of the build-up toward experiencing true intimacy, which might come later. (Most men are fine with a slam-bam-thank-you-ma'am at night before we begin to snore.)

She continued by saying, "Sex is a romantic process that begins in the morning in the kitchen." She meant those previously mentioned sweet and tender expressions of love should start first thing in the morning in the kitchen. But, of course, the men heard it differently and shouted their approval.

"Amen!"

"In the kitchen! Hallelujah!"

Deb became our hero and key spokesperson. Revival broke out! A Pentecostal experience reserved just for men! We were excited!

"Does this mean we can eat the waffles later?"

"Who cares about breakfast! We can always take a break for lunch."

At least, that's what the men heard.

I thought her faux pas was hilarious, but Deb was quite embarrassed.

Revival was soon squelched. She continued, bringing up things like yard work, changing the oil, fixing the roof, painting the kitchen, washing the dogs, and other "prerequisites." The men took notes and tried to establish a timeline. We did the math and drew charts on the wall. We invoked physics. But at the end we were still confused about which requirement should come first. Should I mow the yard first or hold her hand? Sadly we concluded that we all had to eat the waffles.

I know, I know—I'm making sweeping generalizations. But it's all for fun . . . and further research. Yes, physics will still be involved. But, thank God, nanotechnology is coming.

Seriously, I have been blessed with a wonderful and loving wife. She has taught me how to love and be loved. With a woman like Deb, physics and nanotechnology are not necessary. We are one flesh. And that includes sex, but means so much more than sex.

Especially now.

The title of this chapter is "Have Mercy on Me!" I've had some fun with this subject, and I hope you have too. If not, I'm sure I'll hear about it. But true mercy is not a laughing matter.

Mercy is a beautiful word. It means "a compassion or forbearance shown . . ."[1] Like so many definitions, I have to look up other words in the definition to understand the original definition. I get confused. *Compassion* means "a sympathetic consciousness of others' distress together with a desire to alleviate it.."[2] *Forbearance* is another beautiful word. It is defined as "the act of forbearing; a refraining from the enforcement of something (as a debt, right, or obligation) that is due."[3]

So, for me, true mercy involves two words: *compassion* and *refraining*. Also for me, these two words define the status of sex when cancer enters the bedroom.

Cancer is an enemy. It seeks to steal and destroy. It makes Deb sick and threatens her very life. It never leaves our minds. It always has a space reserved in our brains. The pain reminds us of its unyielding presence. Many times "feeling better" is only a brief moment when laughter interrupts or we get lost in a good book. But it can change to "feeling worse" in the blink of an eye.

Deb has gone though this rollercoaster of thoughts and feelings. She shared in an earlier chapter about some men who left their wives because of cancer. Some have affairs and leave their wives hopeless and helpless. These are the women who've been tossed aside. What kind of husband would do this? I've read of several political leaders who left wives suffering with cancer. It makes me very angry when I hear stories like these.

Deb has often told me she cannot imagine going through that kind of trauma on top of everything else. Her heart really goes out to those women. Now, as a fellow cancer survivor, her sorrow and grief for them and for what they're going through is even stronger. She once said, "To not be loved and treated with such respect and compassion during the darkest nights of my cancer is unimaginable."

When Deb was diagnosed with cancer, I received the same diagnosis. I had no tumor, nausea, weakness, or physical pain. But I had it psychologically. At least that's how I felt. It affected almost every area of my life.

Work had to be cut short and interrupted. I gave up vacation days in order to go to doctor's appointments and chemotherapy sessions with Deb. Fun trips with the family ceased due to her nausea. Recreation that took me away for a few days, such as climbing or hiking, stopped. Just finding an hour to go jogging became difficult. I needed to monitor medications and dispense them in the middle of the night.

With cancer, we were starting a long journey together. The roads were going to be rough. We would get lost where no GPS could save us. Mapquest wouldn't work. We would miss towns and key intersections, not knowing whether to turn left or right. Sometimes we would run out of gas altogether and be stranded. At times we would get to our destination and rejoice briefly, only to get lost on the road again. I would be the driver.

During times like these, sex rode in the backseat. It didn't look out the window. It mostly slept.

Using sex as a weapon from either side can be an act of war. Remember the definition of forbearance: a refraining from the enforcement of something that is due. Some men feel their wives are required to provide sex. I do believe a healthy marriage includes it, but it is not the cause of it.

Some men may try to enforce their right to sex when their wife has one of those default headaches. Efforts at enforcement can come in the form of bad attitudes, not being helpful, ignoring, being mean, being angry, and lacking sensitivity. I definitely have been there.

But with Deb's cancer, I have to display this characteristic of mercy. I must have forbearance. She may be too sick (and usually is) when I want it. That definition of forbearance does seem a little harsh to use when it comes to sex. My definition of forbearance might be "not making my wife experience guilt if she doesn't feel like having sex when I want it, and being okay with it and not punishing her verbally or nonverbally when she doesn't feel like doing it." Guilt is the ultimate nonphysical enforcement and the most easily used. It can hurt the most and do the most damage.

I don't want you to think I'm the perfect husband. I am basically and pathetically selfish. I was the baby of the family. My late mother worshiped me. I have two older sisters who worship me. So I got away with everything I did and got everything I wanted. Since Mom passed away a few years ago, I still get everything I want from my sisters.

Sex can be an act of selfishness. Sometimes I am only concerned about my pleasure, not hers. However, her pleasure may be in providing me pleasure. And now with Deb's cancer, her pleasure may not be defined as pleasure at all in the sense of a normal sexual experience.

Mercy sex is the ultimate act of selflessness. I know I've had some fun with that term, but it really is a beautiful expression of love. To refuse it can be an expression of rejection.

I have to think of it this way. Suppose I bought my wife a gift—a very expensive gift. So expensive I had to secretly work an extra job to buy it. Consequently I was tired and beat most of the time. But I kept it up because I wanted to please my wife with this expression of love. The gift meant more to me in the giving of it than it would to her receiving it. Then the big day came. I offered the gift to my wife. She refused it and told me to take it back. How would that make me feel? Terrible, of course.

Mercy sex is like that. Sometimes Deb feels like it is the greatest gift she can offer me. Not only is it about me and my needs, but it is about her and her desire to meet my needs. It is about her giving and not just my receiving.

When it comes to sex, one of the things I've dealt with is a fear that I might hurt Deb physically. After all, she has cancer, scars, rashes from radiation, and other discomforts. I don't want to cause her more pain, or worse yet, break something. I need to know the parameters and, trust me, Deb lets me know.

Communication is extremely important. A healthy man and woman don't often talk about what they like best or need most before, during, and after sex, much less when one of them is sick. It is so important to discuss issues like this when cancer is involved. Some of the things that used to be pleasurable no longer are. Maybe for her nothing is pleasurable anymore. We may go days, weeks, or longer without sex.

Self-control is an act of selflessness too. It honors Deb and puts her feelings above mine. If I truly love her, especially now with her disease, my desires may need to be put in park for a while. The car may still be running, but I'm not going anywhere.

Yes, it can be difficult sometimes. But the best and only answer I have is to be faithful to my vows. Deb knows many men who have found this too difficult. Shame on them. They didn't deserve their wives anyway.

From my studies on religion throughout my life, I am convinced that three things have, for the most part, controlled all of humanity: money, sex, and power. Each one of these can be used for good or evil. Some religions incorporate all of them as part of their theology, and they serve as a sad foundation for their multiplication and exploitation.

I have to understand that sex does not live in my pants. I must always keep in mind that I am a special creation of God, made in His image. I am not some lower animal that has no self-control, governed by some primitive and primeval urge. I must always recognize that God is an ever-present help during difficult times, offering me the grace needed for each day, and the One who constantly reminds me of my love and commitment to my wife.

I read a book many years ago that talked about how to use sexual energy toward something else that has positive ramifications. I found that to be somewhat true. Since I like to jog, I have tried to run longer and harder. I exercise more and take more cold showers. I write more, read more. And yes, I pray more. This helps more than anything and keeps me focused on Deb's immediate needs, not mine.

One of the hardest things I try to do is to help Deb feel beautiful and sexually desirable again when she does not feel that way. Her chest is flat. She knows I always enjoyed that particular anatomical component and that it played a key role in my sexual arousal. Now nothing exists there.

Deb has told me she feels like a freak and wonders how I could possibly want to have sex with her ever again. This breaks my heart. It has probably affected me more than anything she could ever say. It hurts to see how self-conscious she has become. She feels uncomfortable taking a bath, and she tries to keep her eyes off her chest. I know she feels uncomfortable when I glimpse her chest. She feels totally undesirable.

As I mentioned in the prologue, I usually make my annual pilgrimage to Victoria's Secret at Christmas and buy something fun for Deb. Last year I bought pajamas instead of a sexy outfit. Looking back, I should have bought something different. I am sure she was probably hurt and wondered if I was making a statement about her desirability.

I have to think of ways to tell her how beautiful she is. But even more, I think she needs me to treat her the same way I did before her cancer. She needs me to talk to her, touch her, and kiss her the same way as before she was wheeled into an operating room. She needs me to look into her eyes the way I always have and tell her how much I love her.

All of this has led me to a complete reevaluation and a reaffirmation of what true sexual intimacy is all about. It is not about "boobs and butts." It's not about negligees and skimpy teddies that barely hide the "good stuff." It's not succumbing to the culture's definitions of enticement and sexuality. It's about love—agape love. The early Christians used this Greek term in reference to a love that is self-sacrificing, a love that keeps giving with nothing expected in return.

God's intention for sex was all about the intimacy—caring so much for your spouse that you'll gladly sacrifice for her. To love a wife who is going through cancer is so important, especially when the chemo and baldness make her feel so undesirable. Her hormones are all messed up, and the chemo can send her over the cliff into menopause, no matter what age she is. Her sexual desire is zero. Yet my wife continues to give herself to me. That is true love. The intimacy we experience when she gives herself to me—even when she doesn't feel like it—is the truest example of agape love. It is sacrificial.

In modern America we are completely ignorant of the concept that sexuality is so much more than just physical satisfaction. It's that intimacy and communion of spirit. Yes, sex is fun. Yes, it can feel good! Yes, it's exciting and titillating! But it's so much more. It is truly spiritual.

Humor helps us to enjoy the intimacy. We try to make sex fun and to laugh. Once Deb complained to me about how flat she was. "You're no flatter than I am!" I teased. We laughed so hard. Laughter eased the tension. After all, sex isn't something you should cry over.

It is true that a double mastectomy changes the anatomy. I believe it has taken Deb longer to adjust to it than it has taken me. Yes, Deb and I miss the boobs. But to reject intimacy because of physiology is not love. Sometimes the truest intimacy has become holding hands in bed. It's massaging her back instead of her front. It's gently rubbing her arm as she falls asleep. It's holding her tight during one of those pesky panic attacks. Sometimes it's lying silently beside her, just so she can hear me breathe.

For Deb as a cancer patient, the physical satisfaction comes in tenderness, holding each other, and love. It's not the orgasm because that just ain't happening for her right now. We are hoping that will change eventually, but for now it's very difficult. Now when she looks in the mirror before her bubble bath at night, she looks down at her body and thinks, *How could anyone ever want to have sex with me?* Her self-image has changed drastically. Once she was a twelve-year-old girl buying her first bra, putting it on, so proud of herself and thinking, *I'm finally a woman!* Now she has no need to wear a bra anymore. The psychological effect of that reality is unbelievable.

The discussion of reconstructive surgery comes up often. Deb and I are dealing with the possibility. This is a fine line for me. I want it to be Deb's decision, but at the same time, she wants it to be mine. It's similar to when your wife asks you if her new dress makes her look fat (a dangerous subject we'll discuss at length in a future chapter). Basically, if you say yes, you're screwed. If you say no, she thinks you think she's already fat, and you're screwed.

In my opinion, whether my wife has boobs or not is not a deal breaker anyway. But if she feels more beautiful with them, I have to affirm her choice to have them reconstructed. If she doesn't want to go through it, I have to affirm that decision as well. Frankly, my vote is for her not to have the reconstruction. I hate to see her go through the pain of that surgery for a couple of bumps on her chest. Love should not be based upon anatomy.

Through our journey with cancer, we have fallen in love all over again. During the last four or five years, we've struggled through some very rough times. Deb's parents moved in with us for a while, our kids met some difficult challenges as kids often do, and we were both in the midst of mid-life crises, though we didn't acknowledge it at the time. All of these situations collided at the same time and seemed to pull us constantly apart. But our love survived. We made it happen that way.

Before I finish, let me be philosophical for a moment. The term *making love* is used as another way of referring to sex. Some think it sounds much more beautiful than the plain old word *sex*. However, in today's culture, *making love* is used so flippantly and casually. In most movies, a man meets a woman, and after a few drinks, they say, "Let's go make love." Or they tell others they met someone and made love last night.

Sex is not *making* love, as if you're using some wooden preschool blocks to build a fort. Sex is not something you make. It originates out of a love that is already made. And sex is not a litmus test to determine whether a love has been made or not.

For Deb and me, making love began as a picture in a student directory. Making love involved a thousand conversations. It was getting to know each other and respect each other. It took many months to make. Finally we felt our love was made, and we told the world as we stood before God and man and said, "I do."

But that love was only the first story. Our love is still being made after thirty years of marriage, and we will not stop making it until death do us part. Before it is over, we will have a skyscraper! Wow, that sounds like fun, doesn't it? Honestly, sex is just one of a million expressions of the love we've made. Our culture has it totally backward. Sex is not making love.

I've done it. I've written my chapter on mercy sex. And I am so glad it's finished. I've had some fun and probably embarrassed Deb. But as I reflect on all the things I've said, as a man I have come to one simple conclusion.

Mercy sex ain't that bad!

Chapter 9

IT'S A FAMILY AFFAIR

—*Deb*

From the first day of your diagnosis—from the very moment you hear the word *cancer*—your mind freezes. It goes completely numb.

When the shock finally began to wear off, my first thought was: How is this going to affect my family? For weeks I'd been aware of the cancer in my breast, but even as I worked through those initial stages of denial, my thoughts centered on my family. What would change? How would this affect our lives? How would I even tell them about my cancer? The communication process was actually hindered by the diagnosis because I did not want to utter those words: *I have cancer.* I didn't want to admit it. I wanted to stay in the Land of Denial because it was a much nicer place to be.

As I told you in my first chapter, I didn't tell my family immediately. I didn't want to spoil our Thanksgiving. I discussed my concerns with Dick on our way home to Georgia, but once I returned home, I had to face the reality. I knew without question it was cancer by the way it looked.

The first person I told was our daughter, Mary. I told her I was suspicious of a lump I'd found in my breast. I told her I was going to see the doctor that day and admitted I was concerned. Her first response was one I would hear from everyone else: "Oh, you don't have cancer, Mom. Don't worry about it. You worry too much!" Later, I remember telling my sister when I was going to have a biopsy. Her first response was, "Oh, you don't have cancer! Cancer runs in families, and we don't have any cancer in our family!"

Those responses are typical. I suppose it's a form of denial on their part. They have to go visit that Land of Denial too because nobody likes to think about cancer. I'll be honest; it was hard hearing everyone brush it aside with comments like that. I wasn't angry at them, but it felt as if they were minimizing my situation. I was going through something scary! I needed them to take me seriously! I needed them to listen to me and be more empathetic. I wanted them to say, "Oh, Debbie, I know this must be so hard for you. We'll get through this together."

To those closest to me, I kept saying, "I know it's cancer. I've been in this business too long. It is cancer." But even those people didn't accept it.

Dick was the only one who took me seriously. And he was scared.

In a family process, one of the most important things you must do is have honest communication about your disease. That includes everyone in your family—from the youngest child all the way up to the elderly. Even the youngest baby knows something is different; something is just *off* in the home. And even though you can't communicate with babies, you can reassure them by taking care of their basic needs, trying to maintain their regular schedule of feeding and sleeping. The same thing applies to children of all ages.

The communication must be open and honest. Now honesty doesn't mean you have to tell them every nitty-gritty detail. You know your own children, and you tell them in ways appropriate to their understanding. To a two-year-old, you may need to use a doll or a puppet to explain. "Mommy has a boo-boo on her chest," or "Daddy has a boo-boo in his brain." You may put a little Band-Aid on the doll's head. "So Daddy's going to go to the doctor, and we hope it's going to be okay." You don't have to tell them all the details, but you do have to tell them.

It's important to remember that their world revolves around them—their needs, their desires, their safety and security. They want to know that those basic elements are going to be taken care of. It may sound selfish when a five-year-old responds to the news by asking, "Can I still go to Danny's birthday party next week?" But that's his world. That's what's important to him. He feels secure if he knows his life will go on as usual even though Mommy or Daddy is sick. The same applies to teenagers. If your teen's response to the news is "Will I still get to go to the prom?", that's her way of asking, "Will everything be okay? Is my world safe?"

Children also have big imaginations. They engage in a process called magical thinking. Since their world centers on them, if you don't tell them the truth, a lot of times they'll assume they are the magical person who's caused this problem.

Just as children whose parents divorce may blame themselves for the divorce, the child of a cancer patient may think "Mommy is sick because of that time I didn't obey her and come home when I was supposed to the other day."

Maybe Billy goes to bed angry with you, lashing out, "I hate you! I hate you!" When you get sick, he processes that information and thinks it's because he said those mean words in anger, when he didn't really mean it. Maybe Susie heard Uncle Fred talking about her sick father: "If Bob hadn't smoked cigarettes all those years, he wouldn't be sick now." Or she heard Aunt Betty say, "This is God's punishment on Bob for not going to church."

What a terrible message that would send to the child, that God is punishing one of her parents by making him sick with cancer. She then wonders, *Is God going to punish me if I don't say my prayers or go to church?* Such stupid statements can seriously distort a child's image of God.

If adults are whispering about the cancer behind closed doors or around corners trying to keep it from the children, their magical thinking may cause them to think the secret is somehow their fault. They wonder, "Why else wouldn't they tell me what's going on?" They may start having bad dreams. They don't know what to do with these feelings, so they start imagining monsters under the bed or fearing that something terrible is about to happen.

A lot of times parents think it's helpful to spare the child from troubling news, but often that's when more serious problems start. Children are always listening. It's important to be aware of what you're saying, how you're saying it, and what they may be hearing from others.

Most children are strong enough to hear the truth, and they need to hear it. Tell them as much as possible without causing alarm. *These are the things that will change; these are the things that won't change. Your world is secure. Your job is to keep going to school and keep up with your homework. You might help around the house a little more, but otherwise things will stay the same.*

Especially young children still want to interact with the parent who is ill. "Sally, it's your responsibility to take Mommy a blanket. That will be a big help to her!" You give them opportunities to have contact whenever possible.

Teenagers are an entirely different story. By nature, teens want to pull away. But at the same time, they can understand more about the cancer. They too may become fearful, but be honest with them. Teenagers are quick to run to the Internet to search for answers. Some of that information will scare them out of their wits. When they come to you with those fears, be honest with them. "Every individual case is different, sweetheart. You're not going to find any specific case on the Internet like mine, so let's not worry about all that just now."

Even Dick planted himself on the Internet after my diagnosis and tried to become an expert on breast cancer. In fact, at one point he came to me asserting, "I think that lump could have been caused by the seat-belt snapping over your chest when you had your wreck." He'd read something online about such things happening. Again, it was his way of searching for answers, trying to find normalcy instead of allowing himself to think about what might be ahead.

My son, Scott, who was twenty-three at the time of my diagnosis, also immediately went on the Internet, studying everything he could find on the disease until he thought himself quite the expert on all things cancer. He memorized the percentages and quoted them to me. "Your recovery chances are 80 percent with no recurrence, so I think those are pretty good odds." He lectured me on the different medications and their successes through various trials, recommending this one and that to me.

The more information he absorbed, the more secure he felt. It was his way of dealing with the news. The following is his perspective.

Scott

As I sat listening to a seemingly endless slideshow on the exigencies of running a weapons qualification range at Fort Bliss, Texas, my mind and body were somewhere else. I waited anxiously for my phone (which is unauthorized in the classroom) to vibrate as I planned to surreptitiously feign taking a restroom break in order to hear the news.

What would the tests show? Would it be the dreaded C-word? I could not even bring myself to contemplate the idea. I thought to myself, "Surely not! These things don't happen to someone in my family, especially my mom." But when my pocket vibrated jarring me from once again dozing off, little did I know that my concept of life itself would drastically change in an instant.

I entered a whole new world where my perfect life really wasn't so perfect after all. The stories I had seen, the books I had read, and the movies I had watched where the trials and tribulations of the world rear their ugly heads were not so distant after all. No one is immune.

It's said that everyone deals with problems in their own unique way. Some people go through certain stages of grief and depression as they attempt to deal with whatever news they have received. I guess you could say that I followed the typical pattern at first. I jumped full speed ahead on the Denial Express. "Maybe the test was wrong. Maybe we should get a second opinion. This can't be right."

I stayed in this mindset for quite some time, as it was easy to do. I was nearly 2,000 miles away, and it was no problem for me to remain in denial. I did not have to take Mom to chemo, to see the hairs fall out one by one, or watch her come home weak and sick. I knew it was happening, and it broke my heart to hear her tired voice on the other line.

Calling my mother every day was my commitment. Oftentimes I would hang up the phone having heard her tired, yet strong voice on the other line and cry to myself, wishing I could be there to give her the support she deserved.

If I had had the capacity, I certainly would have moved home to be with my family in our time of need. However, the Army is not an organization that provides too many options for personal matters. I was forced to make do with offering support from a distance.

Coming home for the first time after the chemo was complete and seeing Mom's bald head brought the denial phase to an abrupt halt; my mommy was a cancer patient. I had to be strong. I kissed her and hugged her, reminding her that she had all my love.

It was at this point that I entered a new phase of grief and found myself much sadder than before. Each trip home brought new questions I had never before pondered. Would I see her again? Would it be under the worst of circumstances? I vowed to make sure that every opportunity I had to show her how much I loved her would not go idly by. I wanted her to feel special.

When the treatment was complete, my heart filled with a variety of emotions, among them excitement, reserve, and new fear. What if it comes back? I do not know what I would do without her. She has made me the man I am today. I owe everything to my mom and dad, who raised me in an amazing home of which she was the rock. She is the strongest, most loving, and most caring person I know. When we are not promised tomorrow, it makes us cherish much more the moments of today. This sentiment has taken on a whole new meaning in my life.

Upon hearing my diagnosis, our daughter, Mary, was immediately concerned about whether she would get breast cancer. Even though there are some genetics involved, I explained we could have her tested for the BRCA gene (a test to see if she has the gene that would make her prone to developing the disease) to help ease her fears. But initially kids need to be assured cancer is not contagious so they won't obsess over it. Mary shares her reactions below.

Mary

It was a gloomy day in Statesboro, Georgia. The normal heat-drenched, humid sun was nowhere to be found. The afternoon sky was cloudy as I drove to my best friend's house in the country. School had taken its toll. I was a twenty-year-old college student, and my thoughts were focused more on the next party, the next time I could breathe in the laughter of my friends.

My phone began to ring above the blaring radio, and "DAD" flashed across the screen, not unusual because my dad checked in on me often, perhaps more than I wished. His normal hello sounded painful this time, the type of hello that made my heart squirm, waiting for whatever bad news was coming next. I'd only heard this tone of voice a few times in my life. It was like an avalanche you can hear from miles away but you tell yourself it's only thunder, and there's nothing to worry about.

"Your mother has been diagnosed with breast cancer."

The words echoed in my head while I sat at the red light, the avalanche enveloping me. What came next was denial, and the rest of the conversation was a blur. I had no tears, only this hollow feeling and a lump in my throat I couldn't swallow.

Driving alone through the country roads gave me time to think. What would I say to my mom? What exactly did this mean? My hands were shaking as I dialed her number. A soft, teary hello greeted me on the other end. I could tell she'd been crying, and I wanted more than anything to hug her and kiss her, to tell her everything was going to be okay.

That was only the beginning of the nightmare. I've heard people say, "Once one person gets cancer, the whole family gets cancer." I couldn't agree more. I was angry that it happened to my mom, of all people, someone who had dedicated the past twenty years of her life to helping those with cancer and their families, someone who knew so much about the dangers of this horrible disease. I sat there helplessly, three-and-a-half hours away, as more bad news came with every phone call from home. The stages kept getting higher, the tumor bigger.

It seemed like breast cancer was haunting me. On TV, every pink ribbon on the bottom of the screen, every commercial for a walk to raise money, every "I'm a survivor" speech would make me cringe, and I couldn't change the channel fast enough. Even my favorite TV show, *Nip/Tuck*, had an episode on breast cancer and chemo. I hated even thinking about. I wanted to seal it up forever like a box and bury it in the back of my mind.

I busied myself with school and friends, but the box kept getting ripped open with every phone call from my dad. As much as I didn't want to leave my little apartment in Statesboro, I needed to go home and help.

Chemotherapy came next. I watched my mom get weaker and weaker, lose her hair and lose her energy. I felt so helpless. No matter what I did, I couldn't make her pain go away. Cancer seemed like a being in itself, forcing its way into our lives with no intent of stopping. Week after week my mother had harsh chemicals injected into her body, chemicals meant to kill this "being." Even after the chemo, however, the cancer was still there.

The week of my twenty-first birthday, my mother decided to have a double mastectomy. We took a break from all the doctors' appointments and craziness at home to rest with our extended family. I remember her asking my opinion about the procedure, and I assured her I was for it. Anything to "cut out" the chance of this disease taking her away from me.

That night I looked up at the moon shining down on the water, my best friend Elizabeth by my side. I wanted it to last forever, to stay in this moment with my family and friends, to freeze time. I wanted to hold onto everything life threatened to take away.

The day of the surgery seemed like a slap in the face, a reality check. I didn't know the extent to which this would affect my mother until I saw her in the recovery room, her flat chest heavily wrapped. I would never see the same mom again. This horrible cancer had taken pieces of my mother away. As a woman, my heart broke for her. My outlook on life seemed to change that day. My hatred for what was happening kept getting stronger, yet all I could do was sit back and watch.

My father became my guide. His kind words and gentle affection urged me to keep hope. Over the next few weeks my mom couldn't do much, but family and friends surrounded us with much-needed attention. We all wanted this to be the end. Now that the cancer was gone, we wanted to look ahead and never look back.

From that first phone call in Statesboro to now, the word *cancer* still strikes a nerve in me. A cloud still looms in the distance, and I never know when it might start to pour. Although the cancer is gone, my mother fears it will come back. As for now, life with my mom is a precious gift, and every day is a blessing for me. I try not to think about the what ifs because that would be letting this disease run my life. I hope fifteen years from now my mother and I can look back on this as a lesson in life to never take anything for granted.

She is my inspiration, my breath of fresh air. And nothing, not even cancer, is going to take that away from me.

Again, you know your children better than anyone, but you do need to be as honest with them as possible. If you're dishonest with them about the cancer and everything that's going on, then when there's a change or a turn for the worse, they may feel betrayed. "You said everything was going to be fine! You lied to me!" You don't want to be pessimistic, but you have to tell the truth. "We're hoping this treatment will work." They may ask, "But what if it doesn't?" You answer honestly: "Then we'll deal with whatever happens. We'll cross that bridge when we come to it."

Regardless of their age, when children ask the tough questions, be honest. If they ask what will happen if the treatment doesn't work, try turning their question around and putting it back to them. "What do *you* think will happen?" If they answer, "I think Daddy will die," then you talk about that; again, in a way appropriate to their age level of understanding.

"Do I force them to talk with me about my cancer?" parents ask. I always tell them it depends on the individual child. If a daughter has always been introverted or quiet and suddenly becomes mean and nasty, acting out badly, then you know something is going on with her. If an outgoing son suddenly becomes withdrawn, you know there's a problem. Talk with his school teachers, other parents who are involved in his life, your church ministers or youth pastors.

Start a network of support for your children. Be honest with them, explaining the situation with as many details as you're comfortable sharing to solicit their help. A teacher can be on the lookout for dropping grades. A school counselor can keep an eye out for behavioral changes. A church pastor may pick up on the child's despondency or lack of normal involvement in activities. Again, communication is the key. You'll find that most people are more than willing to help in any way they can. Try to keep the child's world as stable as possible.

I also tell parents to watch out for the big changes. I remember one gentleman who told me about his daughter who was a straight-A student and extremely active in her youth group. One day, out of the blue, she stole one of her friend's sweaters. When confronted about it, she lied. "I didn't take it." Her behavior had become radically different. When parents see these kinds of drastic changes, they need to seek out professional help, preferably from a child psychologist.

But with any age child, the best thing to do is to listen. Watch for even the tiniest of clues. Perhaps you're cooking dinner and your child asks, "Are we not going to have pizza any more because it makes you throw up?" Then you know the child is thinking about these things, considering various options through the filter of cancer.

Most often kids are convinced cancer equals death. They don't understand the hair loss. They're extremely sensitive to family issues: if their parents are arguing more or if a parent has to take a second job to make ends meet. They pick up those little clues, and usually it revolves around them—how their world is going to change.

Over the years I have found the biggest problem is that people simply don't want to be honest. It usually stems from the fact that they don't know how to handle the situation. They're scared. They're fearful and full of doubt about the future.

Kathleen McCue, in her book *How to Help Children Through a Parent's Serious Illness*, says, "Always tell all ages Mom or Dad is seriously ill, the name of the disease, and your best understanding of what may happen."[1] Each child handles the situation in his or her own unique way.

Small children have miniscule attention spans. Use art or doll therapy to communicate with them. "Tell me what you're thinking about.

Draw a picture of your daddy and show me what you think will happen to him." You can glean a lot of information from these drawings to learn about their fears or any misinterpretations about what you've told them. If a relative has died and the small child was told, "Uncle George just went to sleep," chances are that child will be scared to death to go to sleep at night! You have to think about what you're saying.

A good way to engage in communication is to have a family town hall meeting. Talk about what's going on. Explain the changes, things they should be aware of. Don't put too many expectations on them. Don't try to make an older child into an adult, suddenly expecting him to be the dad or her to be the mother. Allow them to be children. Don't put the burden on their shoulders. Solicit additional help from friends or extended family. More than anything, let them know you're there for them. "If you have questions, come and ask me." Keep those lines of communication open.

Allow your children to accompany you to some of your medical appointments. It's good for them to see what radiation is, to observe your chemotherapy treatment. They have a tendency to distort things they can't see or understand. Seeing what's actually going on helps them process what you're going through.

Tensions may rise in the home when cancer arrives. As I've mentioned before, cancer exacerbates whatever situation is usually in play. If the home is often filled with arguing and shouting, those tendencies will ramp up as cancer invades the home. Finances may become tight, the patient doesn't feel well and can't handle things like he used to, and his spouse may feel like she has to do everything.

Be cognizant of the message these tensions are sending to your children. Even when kids are used to occasional yelling in the home, under these circumstances you may need to seek out a professional to help calm the tension in the home.

Unfortunately I've heard too many sad stories over the years. Dad says, "I'm out of here. I'm not doing this," after his wife's diagnosis. The kids are left alone with a sick mother who must struggle to care for them and for herself.

In these cases, professional help is a must. Through social workers, through school systems, through churches, through your doctors and caregivers—whatever it takes—get help. Again, it requires that network of support to cover all the bases or people fall through the cracks—especially the children.

Two months after his wife's diagnosis of breast cancer, "Frank" left his wife and four young children, took every dime out of their checking and savings accounts, left her with the mortgage payment, and went to California. Apparently he wasn't interested in sticking around to help her through this disease or to help care for their children. "Dana" spent hours crying in my office.

I kept thinking, *What kind of person could do such a thing?* Through my office, we connected her with different agencies where she could get help and financial assistance. Even throughout her chemotherapy treatments, she continued working half days. Having been through chemo myself, I have no idea how she continued to work in spite of the extreme fatigue and nausea and just feeling so terrible. Even when she occasionally had to miss a day or two, her boss was compassionate enough to work with her, allowing her to keep her job. She had extended family members who were able to help look after the children.

Eventually she lost her home and had to move in with a cousin. The conditions were cramped, but the cousin was supportive and glad to help. It took more than a year for her to get back on her feet and find a place of her own for her family to live. She never once heard from her husband except for the divorce papers he sent her.

Dana was my hero before I had cancer. She's even more of a hero now.

Sometimes situations like these baffle my mind. "Judy" had survived ten years with advance staged cancer. She was from an upper-middle class home and divorced. During divorce proceedings, the judge had ordered her now-ex-husband to pay all her bills so she could stay in her home while she battled cancer. She was now in hospice care, though still at home, wheelchair bound and on oxygen, near the end of her journey.

One day, returning home from an appointment in our office, she found the electricity in her home had been turned off. Her ex-husband had not paid the bill. Without electricity, her oxygen tanks were useless. Late on that Friday afternoon, we had to find a judge who would write a special injunction to make Georgia Power turn her electricity back on even though her bill had not been paid.

As I stood before the judge that afternoon, he was not happy. He had Georgia Power turn her power back on and had her ex-husband arrested. As I have learned through the years, judges tend to be on the side of the patient.

When Judy's doctor heard about the incident, he said, "There's a special place in hell for men like that." I agree.

Here in the Atlanta area, there's an organization of physicians' wives—Women for Women of Cobb County. They raise money specifically for women who are cancer patients. They focus on these women because of story after story like Judy's, in which husbands have run off and left their cancer-stricken wives and children in their greatest hour of need. The funds raised by Women for Women help with rent or mortgage payments, electricity and water bills, grocery bills—wherever there's a need. There are so many heartwarming testimonies of women who've been able to stay in their homes and pay their bills and care for their children because of the contributions of this wonderful organization.

Lots of organizations and churches through the community are available to help cancer patients in these times of need by gathering around them and supporting them. Sometimes they help pay the bills, bring meals to the families, arrange for taking kids to school, or help in any way they can. Often they become like family, giving the emotional, physical, and financial support that is so greatly needed.

Those are the good stories.

When cancer comes into the home, the family encounters significant changes on so many different levels. The subjects we've covered in this chapter are intended to help those families navigate through the dark waters of this disease.

I can't say it often enough: The most important thing to remember is *be honest*. Always.

I find it amazing how many people don't want to be honest about serious illness. When my own father was dying, my mother and older sister did not want to tell him he was dying. One night, as they repositioned him in the hospital bed, a nurse asked, "Mr. Knight, does that feel better for you?" He answered gruffly, "What I want to know is when do I get to go home!" He thought he was in a rehab unit because that's what my mother and sister had told him.

I'd wanted desperately to tell him the truth. But Mom said, "If you tell him the truth, I'll never forgive you, Debbie." I felt absolutely powerless. I walked out into the hall and broke down crying. My sister followed me, asking what was wrong. "It is not fair to not let him know he is dying. He has a right to know. And I want to be able to say goodbye to him."

Two days later as I sat with him, I asked, "Daddy, do you think you're dying?" He answered, "Nah, I'm not going anywhere." Was he really unaware of how sick he was? Or was he just trying to protect me?

I was the last person to see him alive. He was on oxygen, and his breathing was very labored. I held his hand and said, "I promise you I'll take care of Mom," knowing it had been his biggest concern for years. He made no response. I said, "Daddy, I think today you're going to see Jesus. Say hello to Jesus for me, will you?"

Daddy's expression flashed, his eyebrows jumping high on his forehead. And while he said nothing, in that expression it was as if he said, "What?!" As if he had no idea he was dying.

After he died, my mother stayed true to her word. She never forgave me. The last promise I'd made to my father was to take care of my mother. But she moved in with my older sister, and things were never the same between us. Another family trauma only compounded her anger toward me.

A few months later, as she lay near death in the hospital, I went to be with her. Everyone else had left. I was lying there on her bed, holding her hand and telling her how much I loved her. She opened her eyes and scolded me, "Debbie. I'm not going to die!"

Her anger for me had not diminished. She was still so mad at me. After a moment, I said, "Well, I hope not. I really hope not. I just want you to know I love you." She said she loved me too, but in a tone that was ugly. She had still not forgiven me.

It broke my heart, and it still does. I feel like I failed Daddy by not taking care of her, even though she wouldn't let me.

Grieving the loss of a loved one is hard enough, but it's excruciating when guilt is involved. This is why it is so important for people to be able to communicate. To be able to speak freely. To share what's in their heart.

And when the time comes, to say good-bye.

Chapter 10

CANCER COSTS A LOT, AND IT'S NOT WORTH A DIME

—Dick

On a television interview, a famous actress once said that money meant little to her. As long as she could travel anywhere in the world, money was not important in her life. A well-known game show hostess said that her greatest fear in life was running out of cat food.

When cancer arrived in our house, both travel and cat food disappeared.

As a minister, I have counseled hundreds of couples whose marriages were in turmoil. In most cases, the overall issue boiled down to money problems caused primarily by overuse of credit cards and a desire to live above their means. But in some cases other extenuating circumstances were at the root of their money woes—for example, unexpected catastrophic illness.

This is where we are.

Deb always handles the checkbook. This is not a power grab in our relationship. This is because I am not good with numbers, and she is. Most of the time I have no clue how much money we have or need. I just get the sense that it's not enough. She banks online, and I don't even know the password. She opens dozens of bills and places most of them in her purse for attention later. When I'm desperately searching through her purse for a couple of bucks for a medium cup of Dunkin' Donuts coffee, I find that past-due bills have already eaten all the paper money. Great. No coffee. My daily commute is ruined. I'm lucky to find one quarter and a penny in there.

Then I think, *How pathetic is it to be a fifty-seven-year-old man who doesn't even have two dollars in his pocket?* Like a child, I search under the washing machine, in the crevices of the couch, and in the deep recesses of the kitchen drawer. The kitchen drawer is like a graveyard where obscure items go when they die. Every home has one filled with ballpoint pens that don't work, business cards of dead people, recipes that made you gag, dull nail clippers, and a partially melted gumdrop hiding pennies and maybe a quarter or two. One day I will find plutonium in there.

"Honey, have you seen the plutonium? I know I saw it somewhere."

And the funny thing is, she knows.

Yes, my wife is the banker. She writes the checks, balances the accounts, makes deposits, transfers money, keeps the records, and cries. That's the part I hate. She knows how much we have or don't have down to the very penny. I can always tell when we're getting low on money. She sits quietly and stares off into space. Then I ask that stupid question, "Honey, what's wrong with you?" And, as other wives always respond, she says, "Oh, nothing."

Of course, later I find out that "oh, nothing" means we're about to start bankruptcy proceedings.

Deb came from a family that had money. By money, I do not mean that her father and mother were millionaires. Her father owned a very successful business in Fayetteville, North Carolina, and always carried a few hundred dollars in his wallet. I lusted. Even today, I am unsure which president is on the front of a $100 bill. Or maybe it isn't a president? Maybe it's Bill Gates. (Perhaps I can find one underneath the washing machine. I'll get back to you on that.) However, Deb's family certainly had more money than mine. In fact, my family considered anyone who had $10 more than we did to be rich. And that was just about everyone.

Deb had a beautiful home in a nice neighborhood. Her parents sent her to a private college. They paid for her apartment and a new car. She wore nice clothes and had plenty of spending money. Her friends were debutantes and daughters of company presidents. Deb was not pretentious at all. She grew up not worrying about money. This changed, however, when she married me. What a catch I was! She should have thrown me back. And this monetary dynamic has always had an impact upon our marriage.

My dad was an underpaid policeman, and mom was a hosiery mill worker. We never owned our home. We lived in a rented "mill house" on the other side of the tracks. Necks in our neighborhood were not only red, they were crimson.

Have you ever gone back to your hometown after being away for a long time to see where you grew up? I had not been back to Concord, North Carolina, for twenty years because my late mom and dad had moved to Raleigh to live near some of their grandchildren. So whenever I visited Mom and Dad, I didn't actually go back "home."

When Scott and Mary were in grammar school, we went back to Concord. I wanted to show the kids my hometown. I wanted to show my son where I played baseball, the creek where I spent hours trying to find crayfish, and the tree I fell out of. I wanted my daughter to see the elementary school I attended and the homes of my grammar school sweethearts (even though they all broke my heart). I wanted Scott and Mary to experience a hundred other places and people I remembered.

I turned left from Spring Street onto Buffalo Avenue. I always hated that name. I don't recall ever seeing a buffalo on my side of town. Only a few field rats and cats. Those two always seemed to hang around together.

There I was at that stoplight. It was still hanging a little too low and crooked. I hated that light. It always caught me. And after twenty years it caught me again. It remembered.

The same Church of God was to my right. I was always scared when I rode my bicycle by it on Sunday mornings when my family didn't go to the Baptist church. They seemed to be singing ridiculously loud, and the preacher yelled a lot. I thought he was mad at me. Later I came to realize that they just really knew how to praise God!

When I drove by the house where I grew up, the first thought that came to my mind was, *Were we really that poor?* I wondered how in the world five of us could even fit inside—with only one bathroom—and have I mentioned that I have two older sisters? They always won the bathroom wars. I had to wait and wait and wait for my turn. Thankfully, there was always the backyard.

It's funny. Things looked so much smaller than I remembered. Our house, our yard, hills I slid down, the field I played in, and the creek all seemed tiny. When I was little, yards and fields were enormous. A hard-hit baseball would never leave our front yard. The creek was a raging river. The only things larger were the trees Dad and I had planted when I as nine. Now they reached into the sky like giant redwoods.

I felt old.

On some Sunday afternoons Dad would say, "Let's go ride down Bloody Road." This referred to the rich part of town where doctors, lawyers, and successful businessmen and women lived. Deb would have lived on a Bloody Road. Why he called it that, I'll never know. Why did we drive down Bloody Road on those Sunday afternoons? I'll never know that either. But the homes were beautiful and enormous. Maybe he was dreaming of a bigger home and a better life for us. Sometimes we forget that moms and dads have dreams too. Many unfulfilled.

Yes, our home was poor. But it sure didn't seem that way growing up. The neighborhood was not as pretty as I thought it was back then. Maybe that's because Mom used to tell us we were rich in love, and that was more valuable than all the gold in the world.

I share all of this because of the differences Deb and I have regarding money. She was raised with it. I wasn't. She worries, and I don't think about it that much.

Cancer costs a lot, and it's not worth a dime. The expenses are overwhelming. Chemo, biopsies, radiation, shots, MRIs, PET scans, and medications all know your mailing address. They show up often like Publishers Clearing House letters, pizza flyers, and oil-change discount coupons. One of Deb's shots cost $7,000. She got five of them. We asked what was in those shots and were told it was plutonium. They could have gotten it out of our kitchen drawer.

All of this puts pressure on us.

Disease and lack of money are close friends. Because of cancer, they both live in our house like unwelcome in-laws. They eat our food and sleep in our bed. They lie around on our couch and watch our HD television—without the HD channels we had to give up. They control the remote and make us watch what they want to watch. We don't like the channels they choose.

According to the Bible, man's duty is to take care of his wife. The husband is the provider. He is the hunter. He brings back into the cave the bloody left hindquarter of a giant snaggled-toothed jackalope and a box of Hamburger Helper. You've probably seen the more evolved jackalopes at places like Cracker Barrel on a display just under Billy the Talking Bass. As a Neanderthal chauvinistic snaggled-tooth pig, he says to his wife: "Me providem you food, woman. You cook." That sounds good. But I can't seem to find that in the Bible. I know it has to be in there somewhere because I paid good money for a leather-back edition.

When cancer came to live with us, I became both the hunter and the cook. The Food Network is my new best friend. In fact, when your wife is sick, you're the cook, housecleaner, shopper, errand boy, dog feeder, nurse, and everything in between.

But to be honest, it is such an honor to be all those things for Deb.

I am a minister by trade or "calling." Calling sounds more significant. The reason I chose to be in the ministry was to get fabulously wealthy. Not. I'm still waiting. Most ministers I know are broke and feel like they are supposed to be broke. So do their church members. They feel it is more spiritual. After all, Jesus had no place to lay His head. What was good for Jesus is good enough for the preacher, right? If being broke is a sign of true spirituality, I must be a very godly man.

If only I could become one of those TV health-and-wealth preachers. Then I could make some money—*real* money. I'd need a silk suit and a Rolex watch, though I hear a prayer cloth can bring in over $50! And a small bottle of Jordan River water brings in even more.

If I were one of those rich preachers, I could promise instant healing. Because of "seed faith gifts" I could guarantee it. Seed faith gifts usually refer to money sent to that preacher's ministry (or business). I wonder if they've ever had cancer. Did they heal themselves? With those kinds of promises, I would imagine they should live forever. But they don't, and many of their promises are not realized by others.

Even though I am in the ministry and I disagree with most of their unverifiable promises and modus operandi, I so want it to be true. I want to send enough money to them and have enough "faith" so Deb will get her healing. I want to go to one of their anointed camp meetings or lay my hands on the TV to get it. I want it to be that easy for cancer to leave Deb. I would do anything for her.

However, I have counseled dozens of disappointed believers whose hearts were shattered because they or their loved ones were not healed as promised. They ask, "Why?" Most come to one conclusion: Something is wrong with their faith.

I know not all of these preachers are like those I have described. I apologize if I seemed to lump them in all one box. If you have been healed by God through one of their ministries, I am thankful for that.

When loved ones are ill, all avenues may be explored. I just hope God does not have a calculator.

As we face the financial burdens of cancer, it is hard as the chief bread winner not to be able to bring Deb real financial security. We have little extra money. As her husband, I feel guilty for not being able to give her the best of everything, especially now. I look around the house and see the old furniture. I watch her read decorating magazines, dreaming of ways to make her home more beautiful despite that old furniture. And now with the future uncertain, it makes me sad to think maybe nothing will change.

At times I am filled with regret that I did not provide her with the nicest home or most expensive car. I wish I had a million dollars in the bank so she would not worry. If anything happens to her, how could I deal with not giving her those things? The older I get, the less likely it is that I will find a pot of gold. But for Deb I will keep on trying. She loves me and never complains.

When Deb lost her job, we lost half of our income. Cancer came along and started eating away at the other half. Co-pays and prescriptions come daily. Road trips to the doctor empty our gas tanks. Money in our savings account disappears. Retirement funds are robbed. We find that we have more month than money. Jesus once said that the love of money is the root of all evil. Others have said that the lack of money is. We're caught somewhere in between.

The buck stops with me. I have a job and thank God for it. Without it, we would lose our home, our cars, our food and clothing. Maybe not the clothing, but when your wife has cancer, clothes don't come off that often. When they do, it can be quite enjoyable. (See chapter 8.)

The added job stress and the pressure to produce change your attitude. You must keep your job at all costs. Sometimes I get desperate and try too hard. Other times I am so depressed I can't focus or function. Most of the time my thoughts are about Deb and how hard it is for me to be at work while she's sick at home. There was a time I worried she might never work again or have a job where she makes good money.

Keeping insurance has become my driving force. Without it, I have no clue what we would do. I once asked Deb what happens to people who have a catastrophic illness such as cancer when they have no insurance. Without blinking an eye, she said they lose everything but their primary residence and means of transportation. It surely is comforting to know we will always have a place to stay and a car to drive while we sit and starve in our living room. She has counseled many patients who were in this situation, and she knows their horror stories.

A recent study of cancer patients revealed more than 25 percent have used up most or all of their savings to pay for cancer treatment. Many pass up recommended treatments because they're just too expensive. It's also been reported that almost 20 percent of Americans have trouble paying their medical bills.

It's not my intention to make an argument on any aspect of the health-care debate. These are serious issues, and I'm not an expert on either side of the aisle. Best for me to keep my opinions to myself.

Letters from insurance companies can be blessings or curses. After reading the statements and balances, we are elated when all procedures are covered and paid in full. At other times we discover that some procedures are not. The insurance companies may consider them unnecessary or duplicated. Deductibles were not met. Phone calls and explanations do not satisfy. When all else fails, we tell them the check is in the mail and they should get it sometime in the next decade. "The postal service sure is slow . . . "

Family members may be tapped. This causes some embarrassment, and you may feel like a total loser. I have. But I'm thankful my sisters are rich and not stingy. Sharon and Pat are the greatest sisters a brother could have as well as sisters-in-law to Deb. So are our brothers-in-law, Don and David. They live on a Bloody Road in Carolina Beach. I remember when Deb was first diagnosed with cancer, they immediately gave us $1,000 to help cover the co-pays they knew were coming. We didn't even have to ask. And they have provided more as we have needed it. They have bought wigs, filled our freezer with food, and picked up dozens of restaurant tabs.

In May 2009, during the height of Deb's chemotherapy when she was so sick, her sister Joan came to visit her. She's a salesman for a furniture company, and it's hard for her to get away. She doesn't get paid if she's not selling.

Just two short months later, when it was determined Deb would have to have a double mastectomy, Joan wanted to be there for her sister again. When she told her boss she needed to take a few days off to go back to Atlanta, he was less than cooperative. She explained her sister's situation and the seriousness of the surgery, to which he replied, "You need to get your priorities straight and decide which is more important—your job or your family."

"I already have," Joan answered. She walked out and never went back.

Deb was recovering from her mastectomy on her birthday. Joan and Deb share the same birthday, just three years apart, and it meant so much to Deb that her sister was there. I remember Deb opening her birthday gifts in the hospital and looking over to see Joan crying. Deb was still really out of it from the medication, but even then, I knew she was wondering if she would be around for their next birthday.

Support from family is so important. Patients and their spouses have to understand the tremendous sacrifices their families and care-givers make for us. For some people, the sacrifice is big, such as the loss of a job. For others, the sacrifices are small but still important, such as taking time to call every day or write notes.

When cancer hit, our dreams were put on hold. Deb and I want to move to Carolina Beach where my sisters live. With cancer and less money, we have to stay put for a while. That could mean years. Don't get me wrong, we love our home, and we're thankful for it. It may be good for a second or third mortgage if we need it. Oh, I forgot—we've already been there, done that, and took pictures. But for now we must live close to her doctors and treatment centers as she battles this disease.

Maybe one day we'll get to Carolina Beach. It will be one day. I promise.

As I said earlier, Deb knows the account balances. She processes and pays the bills. She floats the checks. She stays in a constant state of financial terror. She knows when the payments are due and which ones to pay first. This is not fair to her. With cancer, any kind of extra stress produces uncomfortable results. It shows up as depression, anxiety, anger at her job loss, and regrets that we didn't save enough money. Although this is not my strong suit, I must ease some of that burden by helping to take care of expenditures and bills. I will just have to find where she keeps the checkbook.

At many financial planning seminars, the leader teaches that to become financially free you have to have six months' worth of income in your savings account, pay cash for a car, pay off your home in fifteen years, send your kids to private schools, use no credit cards, and tithe on the gross. Good idea if you are from another planet.

The financial effects of cancer may be far reaching. We've had to use credit cards, miss a few tithes (make that, many tithes), and tell our daughter we could not afford to pay her college tuition. We've lost much of our savings, and like many couples, we are ninety days away from bankruptcy. I wish I could have the fees and travel expenses paid to that seminar leader. That would help.

We have to go without creature comforts. That seems so trite when so many people in the world do not have clean water or enough food to eat. I'm almost embarrassed and ashamed to talk about these kinds of comforts. Cable television channels are gone. Eating out has become a thing of the past. New clothes aren't in the budget. Real nails replace acrylic nails. Blonde highlights fade to brown. Cars go unfixed. Beans, rice, bologna, cereal, and peanut butter replace rib-eyes and baked potatoes.

At work, several of us make a procession to the local mall at 11:35 a.m. for lunch. Why we always go to the mall for lunch is a question for further discussion. There are dozens of other places around town to eat that surely are better. The usual Burger King, Subway, and Chik-Fil-A are among the gourmet eating establishments there. But by far, the best of the bunch is the Cajun Grill. They serve fried rice, mixed vegetables, and bourbon chicken among other delightful dishes for only $6.09 (if you just drink water). The food swims in a sea of garlic and monosodium glutamate. Definitely healthy. There's also a weird taste of inexpensive olive oil that makes it slide down the throat. No need for chewing. I came up with a different name for the bourbon chicken. I call it liquor chicken. The servers always look at me funny when I order it this way.

Since battling the war of the budget and losing, I skip going out to lunch with the guys from time to time. I can save about $30 a week by doing this. Add that up over a month and it equals about half our car payment. Sometimes I make up excuses about why I don't join them regularly anymore. I tell them I'm going to work through lunch because I have so much paperwork to finish, or I'm going to grab a quick bite later. "I ate a big breakfast and just ain't hungry" serves as a good one from time to time.

But I hate when one of my co-workers has a birthday and everyone goes to lunch together. We divide up the check and treat the birthday boy or girl. Why is it when folks are treated for their birthday, they always seem to order the most expensive item? Several times I've made up similar excuses, but other times I can't get out of it. I look for the cheapest thing on the menu no matter where we eat.

I always like it when someone recommends going to Five Guys for a hamburger. Free peanuts! Usually I order a hot dog (cheapest) instead of a hamburger and load up on the peanuts. At Five Guys, I try to sit beside people who order French fries because they give you so many it's impossible for one person to eat them all. No one really knows my devious reason for doing that . . . I don't think.

Don't get me wrong. I'm not in the poorhouse yet, but I need to save all I can. I still go to lunch with the guys from time to time. But I've discovered the mother lode of cheap lunches: Cup-O-Noodles. You can buy a case of them at places like BJ's or Costco for pennies on the dollar. I can eat lunch for less than fifty cents a day for up to a month. Yum. Cup-O-Noodles taste better with snaggle-toothed jackalope than Hamburger Helper. Have you seen one? I'll take it to work with me and eat it with peanuts.

We save money anywhere it can be saved. We're still trying to find some. I'll look in the kitchen drawer again underneath the plutonium. We must hide as much away from cancer as we can. This disease has an insatiable appetite.

Money can be a problem, and it certainly is for us. Who knows, maybe the sale of this book will solve that problem. Send a copy to everyone you know. Send it to strangers. Please! We'll even autograph it for no extra charge!

We will make it through this. We have to make it through this. There are no other options.

In any case, we are rich in love. And to tell you the truth, that will always be enough.

Chapter 11

ON FEAR, FAITH, AND CANCER

—Deb

"John" sat up in his hospital bed as I walked into his room. He seemed a little shaken, and I could see the concern in his eyes. The doctor had diagnosed John with prostate cancer. He was scheduled for surgery early the next morning.

He was a construction worker, a big, brawny man with a thick mustache covering his upper lip. His face was tanned, his hands calloused and scarred. He'd worked hard all his life to provide for his wife and two teenage daughters who adored him.

After a brief conversation about his family, I asked him what he was feeling at that moment. He paused then said, "I feel sort of out of control." He looked down as tears filled his eyes. "I've never had a problem I couldn't fix myself. And today, I feel kind of helpless." He swallowed hard. "I feel scared," he whispered.

Fear is a normal reaction to cancer. Simply put, fear is an emotional response to anticipated or real danger. In this case, danger has taken the form of cancer. An invisible invasion has occurred in the body. It often arrives unexpectedly and at the worst possible time. Although it may be microscopic, the threat to personal well-being is larger than life.

Fear is an inherent companion of cancer. Treatments, pain, physical changes, hair loss, more bad news, surgery, financial problems, uncertainty about the future, and even death are all real fears many patients experience. As a result, feelings of panic, anxiety, doubt, worry, helplessness, and even emotional paralysis often occur. Being nervous, tense, and on edge is quite common.

Many cancer patients have a difficult time expressing their fears. Some try to deal with their fears through denial. They think that if they ignore the disease and seek to live a "normal" life, it will simply go away. That's the beauty of denial. It stuffs your fears into a box for the time being because you can't handle the overwhelming shock. You have to sneak it away somewhere safe. Eventually, of course, the disease will surface and the fears will rise.

Just as John felt out of control, so did I. As much as I wanted to be in control, even at the very beginning when I was diagnosed, I could not. Eventually I had to let my fears seep out of that box. I envisioned it as letting the air out of a balloon. You have to let it go. You have to do something about it.

Taking on the action of the treatment helps dispel some of the fears, though they keep sneaking back up. Is this treatment going to work? Why do I have to go through all this pain? For me, my biggest nemesis was the knowledge factor I mentioned previously—knowing what was ahead. As soon as I had my biopsy and my lymphadenectomy (where they took out the lymph nodes to determine what kind of chemotherapy I would have), knowing that I had two or more lymph nodes present meant I'd have to have chemo, I'd have to have a port—all of it suddenly fell onto the path before me.

I remember lying on the bed crying, not out of the instantaneous fear that accompanies the diagnosis of cancer, but because this demon of knowledge consumed me. I had seen so many other patients. Their stories of pain and suffering would reverberate in my memory. They had told me how the lymphadenectomy was so much more painful than a mastectomy. While I'd also heard good stories from patients who'd been encouraged by the lymphadenectomy because it gave them good news that the cancer would not spread, it was the pain stories that filled my thoughts.

And how many times had I heard of patients being hospitalized because their ports became infected? I'd visited them, assuring them the round of antibiotics would help them feel much better soon. Some of their infections were so severe the port had to be removed and placed in their arms. That too could get infected, requiring even more treatment.

These thoughts ran through my mind as my own port was placed. They'd told me how much it hurt, and I was allergic to most pain medication. How would I manage the pain? I'd also seen their bruises, some so bad they had to be iced.

Thousands of stories swarmed through my head, making my fears constant. And while all of my patients had feared the unknown, my fears rose because of the known. The medical world had taught me too much. In reliving the stories I'd heard in counseling sessions, the truthfulness of each of their statements became reality for me. If I'm honest, I'd always assumed many of them had exaggerated their experiences. Sometimes in the back of my mind I assumed they were spinning a good story. But, oh, how they weren't. Their truth now became my reality.

One such story came from a young woman I'll never forget. "Bethany" was single and worked for a large home-improvement store. Her greatest fears were not just focused on her breast-cancer diagnosis or the pending effects of chemotherapy, but on her financial situation. She had to work to keep her insurance, but would she be able to work while undergoing chemo?

The Family Medical Leave Act grants eligible employees up to a total of twelve workweeks of unpaid leave during any twelve-month period, but that doesn't pay the bills. For a single person that's not an option. Her company generously allowed fellow employees to donate hours to her to use for time off. And while such a policy is a tremendous blessing, it still could not fulfill all her necessary medical leave.

Bethany's whole perspective was based on these financial concerns. Yes, she was afraid of dying, but she was far more worried about supporting herself throughout her cancer journey.

Recently I ran into Bethany at the mall. When she finally recognized me, despite my short, short hair, her eyes flew open wide, and she hugged me over and over. She asked how I'd been. As I began to tell her about my own battle with breast cancer, I realized my eyes had filled with tears. I didn't want to tell her I, too, was a breast cancer survivor! She was so kind and gracious, yet after we parted, I hurried to my car where I cried and cried. And yet I still have no idea why I hated having to tell her of my cancer.

When I started my new job a few months ago, I didn't tell anyone I worked with about my cancer. During the hiring process the personnel staff reminded me that by law I did not have to disclose my cancer. I was glad because I wanted to be known as the Cancer Survivor's Coordinator, not the breast cancer survivor. I did not want to be labeled by my disease, and I still don't. Perhaps it's a form of denial, but as I've said to my doctors many times, "I do not want to be the patient." Yes,

I'm a cancer survivor, and I'll be a cancer survivor patient the rest of my life. But I don't want to be.

There again, the loss of control. Even as a Christian, I know that I must hand my fears over to God, and I do. But I take it back from Him probably twenty times a day. I want the control even though I can't have it. It belongs to Him.

Chemotherapy ushers in a fear unique unto itself. How would I feel after each treatment? How would I feel the next day? How would I live day to day? Sometimes it became a microcosm of living hour to hour, minute to minute.

When I worked in Clearwater, Florida, I had a patient who'd gone through a stem cell transplant. She told me the chemo made her feel so bad that it once took her all day to pick up a Kleenex off the floor. After my own chemo, I recalled that discussion. It would take me an hour to turn my head on the pillow. I'd stare at the same leaf for hours upon hours, feeling so miserable. Sleep could not take the agony away.

I remember other patient stories of lying on the couch, time passing so slowly and thinking, *This pain will never end.* During those days, my joy came the hour Dick would come home from work. I'd focus on that all day long because I knew he would take care of me. He would fulfill my every wish. Sometimes the only thing that sounded appetizing would be something he'd have to drive to the store to get for me. By the time he'd come home, I would no longer want it. But knowing he was there to care for me was all I lived for on those long days.

Those were the days the patient stories filled my mind. Not the good ones—those rare few who cheerfully accepted their disease—but all the negative ones. After all, that's why most of them came to see me. To tell me how bad the pain was. To tell me of their financial crises. To tell me of giving up on chemotherapy because they could no longer bear the side effects. To tell me of children failing in school because they were so scared of losing their mother or father. On a continuous loop, the stories played over and over in my head.

As my own fears increased I noticed they seemed to be relegated to the next event. The countdown of chemo—*only four more chemos to go . . . three more chemos to go . . .* The anticipation of completing the "Red Devil" treatments (Adriamycin) that makes you feel so horrible. Looking forward to Taxol treatment because that meant I was done with the Red Devil! It was supposed to be so much better—not! Oh, it was better, but it was still chemo.

One of my worst fear experiences came one night when I had an episode of syncopy (fainting). I woke up in the middle of the night and needed to go to the bathroom. When I stood up, I immediately passed out, falling on my bedside table, breaking it and the lamp on it. Dick jumped up to help me, got me back in bed, and checked me over. A bruise was already appearing on my arm.

He drifted back to sleep, but I lay there crying the rest of the night, convinced that the blackout was surely caused by brain mets (secondary brain tumors, called metastases, spreading from other organs— in my case, my breast). At one point, my tiny Chihuahua, Belle, crawled out from under our covers and licked my tears away, as she so often did.

Again, it was my knowledge that terrified me. I was already planning my funeral. I was already planning how to live the remaining months of my life. I would be Stage IV with brain mets, and treatments would cease. No further treatment would be necessary.

The next morning I called my oncologist. Dr. McCoy quickly scheduled a brain MRI that afternoon at 4 o'clock. By 6 o'clock, relief washed over me when the report came back clear. Still, the horror and dread of those hours lying in bed with my thoughts, then later waiting for the results of the MRI, literally rocked me to my core.

After seeing a cardiologist and getting a clean bill of health heart-wise, I was sent to an ear, nose, and throat specialist who found crystals that had formed in my inner ear, causing me to black out. The problem could be easily cured by physical therapy. It was a rather odd malady, but totally unrelated to my cancer. The timing seemed like a sick joke, ironically coinciding with my chemotherapy. But the episode amplified the fear of dying from that point on. Yes, I'd thought about dying and leaving my family and friends, but not this soon.

Many of the fears associated with cancer are justified. It's a disease that should be taken very seriously. However, some of the fears are unjustified. Many of the things we fear may never even happen. Not everyone loses their hair. Not every tumor continues to grow, and not everyone gets worse. Even if some of the things we fear actually happen, many times they're not as bad as we thought they'd be.

The fear of recurrence that may lead to death is usually the most intense fear that cancer patients experience. Cancer has become a synonym for dying in our culture. But this is not always a valid association. Cancer is not an automatic death sentence. Medical procedures and treatment options have advanced dramatically, and the survival rate is very good for many cancer diagnoses.

Perhaps the best way to combat fear is to take definitive action. Do something that puts you back in control. You feel helpless after cancer takes control of your life, but trying to live a normal life will help those fears. Undergo the prescribed treatment regiments. Eat right and exercise. Get the rest you need. Read about your disease and become a student of it. Find out what others have done that has proven beneficial. Control those things in life that you can.

Even after total treatment, sometimes these episodes of fear will creep back in. When you get dizzy or have a headache, you automatically think, *Oh, my gosh, I've got brain mets!* A hip pain makes you think the cancer has spread—never mind that you actually just sat too long in a strange position or took a longer than usual walk. Your first thought is always, *It's spread.*

Not long ago, I had a frightening dream. That day I'd heard about a new breakthrough treatment for brain cancer, called Gamma Knife, at a local hospital. I wondered if some day I might have need of that treatment. I'd also felt bad all day long, fighting a headache and dizziness, no doubt caused by those crystals in my inner ear. But that little dragon of fear popped up its ugly head, taunting me: *You're going to die! It's in your brain now!* All these thoughts swirled in my head through the course of the day and followed me into my dreams that night.

In my dream, my family and I were in our den, much as we were gathered during the holidays. They were all around me, laughing and talking and having a great time. I tried to tell them I'd just learned I had brain mets. I could see Dick, chatting with someone, and he threw back his head in laughter. I kept trying to reach him, but I couldn't. I felt as if I was in a huge bubble, and I couldn't poke through it to reach him!

The next day the dream haunted my thoughts, as bad dreams often do. When I arrived home, exhausted after a long day's work, I saw Dick wearing the same outfit he had on in my dream. I immediately began to cry. "Dick, I'm so afraid of dying!" He pulled me into his arms and listened while I told him about my dream. Tears spilled down his face as he promised not to let me go. We cried together for twenty minutes, once again gripped with this despicable, relentless fear.

Dick responded the best possible way. He held me, promising he'd be there for me, assuring me we'd get through this together. I've told my patients so many times, when the fear of death is scaring you, talk it through. I tell their caregivers to hear them out, never rebuffing them with comments like, "Don't be silly; you're not going to die." Patients need to be able to freely express the fears they're experiencing.

Dick spent the rest of that evening comforting me. I'm so blessed to have a husband who understands how much I need to work through my fears and who allows me as much time as it takes to do that.

Often people find their faith reawakened along their cancer journey. One of the names of God is Jehovah Rapha, the God Who heals. I explain to my patients that the healing may not be of the disease itself, but it may come as the comfort we need to dispel our fears. No, He may not take away every single fear we have, but He offers a comfort that allows us to release them into His control.

I remember one time praying out loud on my way to have a bone scan. I had been experiencing severe back pain and was once again fearful the cancer might have spread. The moment the last word of my prayer was out of my mouth, I heard church bells ringing. I smiled because I knew God had given me a sign. I had always loved the sound of church bells. He knew that, of course. But how often do we actually hear them ringing as we drive in the chaos of traffic? He was reminding me in that moment, "I am with you!"

Later, lying on my back during my bone scan, I felt such calm assurance, knowing that I was not alone. He was with me. Thankfully, the scan revealed that the cancer had not spread.

These are the ways God reveals His comfort to us. Just as Dick held me in his arms and comforted me after my frightening dream, God holds us in His arms, comforting us. He spoke to me that day, comforting me in the simple beauty of church bells ringing.

The fear of recurrence is still very strong, and each person has to learn how to control these fears their own way. I tell my patients they can't let fear "drive the car." They have to figure out the best way to corral their fears. I can't tell them specifically, with a one-size-fits-all answer. Instead, I ask them, "What's your formula? What has helped you in the past to overcome problems or situations?"

My own personal formula included making notations in the margins of my Bible. Alongside psalms or other meaningful verses I'd write specific instances of prayer. When my father was very ill, I made a note beside Psalm 91:4, which says, "He shall cover you with His feathers, /And under His wings you shall take refuge" (NKJV). While

Dad was lying there, I remembered that image of God covering His children with His wings, protecting them. I prayed that verse for my father and made a note in my Bible: *This is Daddy's psalm.* My father recovered from that illness, and every time I see that note in my Bible, I'm reminded of how God ministered to me at that time. These notes have become my faith journey. This is my formula; it's the place I go to remind myself how to overcome my fears.

I've also always told my patients about the importance of exercise. Recent studies have shown a 25 percent decrease in recurrence among cancer survivors who walk one to three hours per week at a leisurely pace. Those who walk more than three hours a week can reduce the chance of recurrence by 50 percent.[1]

That's a huge motivation to get out there and get moving. But not only does exercise help fight recurrence, the sheer benefit of those endorphins energizing your body works wonders to make you feel better. That's something you can control and you can do. The more things you can control—whether it's what you choose to eat or the determination to drink more water or laugh more—the better you will feel about being in control.

Yes, the little demons of fear will pop up now and then, and you have to deal with them. You can't stuff them deep inside. They'll only pop up somewhere else later. Again, I remind caregivers to let the patient talk. Don't smother them with platitudes of brighter days or statements like "just think of how far you've come!" At the moment the patient feels so bad that they can't even think in those terms. To continually gloss over the reality of their pain does not help. Just knowing that you're there and you understand is what they need most.

For some cancer patients, journaling their thoughts and feelings helps them get through the dark times. Journal entries don't have to be lengthy. Even a single thought or a sentence or two expressing what's on your mind can be cause for reflection later. By reading through these entries, you can often spot patterns of thoughts and behaviors—both good and bad—that can be insightful. By analyzing such notations, you can learn to focus on the positive ones.

Getting connected is a good way to combat fear. In my new job at the Cancer Survivor's Network, we find that, by working with others and reaching out to those in need, patients take the focus off themselves and their own problems, even if only for a while. Such volunteer work can be extremely therapeutic.

Others find help by going back to work. It's b
beneficial for me to get back to work, even though it'
ically. It keeps my mind active. People often ask me
in oncology now that I've had cancer. Ironically, v
cancer survivors is not a burden to me. It actually helps me by
ing on their cancer and helping them through it instead of focusing on
my cancer. It's my job, my career, and one that I love.

Communication is another important tool for staying positive and
combating fears. The Internet offers thousands of blogs and chat rooms
where people can share their stories and learn from each other how to
get through the various perils of the disease. Sometimes the simplest
tidbit of information or a helpful suggestion can make a world of difference. But I'm always quick to warn my patients that these same
sources may also include some depressing or negative postings as well
as misinformation, so it's best to be cautious.

CaringBridge.org is a wonderful source of online support. Patients
and caregivers set up private personal Web sites to stay in touch with
family and friends during their serious health crisis. It provides an easy,
centralized way to provide news about the patient's situation—once
again empowering the individual to control something, in this case the
flow of information.

Patients can become exhausted having to tell the same information
over and over. I've always told my patients they don't have to answer
the phone every time it rings. By posting online, they can stay in touch
without constantly having the phone glued to their ears. Caring-
Bridge.org also includes a guestbook where friends and family can post
messages of encouragement, prayers, and other means of support. Over
half a million people connect through the Web site every day.

Support groups offer another avenue of help to cancer patients and
caregivers. Studies show that people who attend support groups have
less chance of recurrence than those who do not. You can find support
groups through oncologists, churches, the American Cancer Society,
or simply by searching the Internet for a group in your area. Visit different groups to find one where you feel comfortable, one that fits your
personality best and offers a positive dynamic.

Sometimes when you talk to God it feels as if He's silent, but He's
always aware of your situation. He promised in Hebrews 13:5: "I will
never leave you nor forsake you" (NKJV). Remember, some of the
greatest men of the Bible had bouts with fear. David was afraid of Saul.

s was fearful of Og, King of Bashan. Joshua feared the King of . The list goes on and on. They all came to understand that God was greater than their fears, and He would give them the resources they needed to overcome them. He will do the same for you.

What do you fear the most right now? Take a moment and make a list of the things that are making you fearful. Date your list and keep it where you can refer to it from time to time. Sometimes just seeing your fears in print helps you to put them in perspective.

God already knows about your fears, and He wants to help you. Talk to Him now.

> Lord, I'm scared today. My fears surround me, and I feel overwhelmed by them. I seem helpless to get rid of them. Just when I think I'm relieved, my fears come back in full fury. Help me to find a place of relief today, free from the bondage of my fears. Place me in Your strong arms and shelter me. Let me experience Your perfect love. Be my strength and my shield. Thank You, Lord.

Sometimes, meditation can be a tremendous source of comfort. Many Christians mistake meditation for some kind of New Age or metaphysical exercise. But the practice of meditation and visualization, particularly when you focus on your relationship with God, can be a uniquely spiritual experience. I have used the following exercise in many conferences and support groups to help my patients learn the practice of meditation.

Go to a special place without fear and read the following story slowly. Read it again, and after you have finished, close your eyes. Reflect on what you have just read and let your mind take you there.

Imagine you are lying on your back in the middle of a large open field. There is nothing in the distance but soft, rolling hills. The lush, green grass is cool beneath your shoulders. The sky is a brilliant blue, and the sunlight is warm on your face. A quiet, gentle breeze glides over your body like a whisper. The only sound you hear is the trickle of a stream, its waters dancing over smooth stones. The sound relaxes you. Your surroundings refresh you. You sense that God is watching you from heaven, shepherding you with His presence and calming your fears. In His Spirit, He reaches down and wraps His arms of love around you. You feel His strength and power. There is nothing to fear now, for God is with you.

The Bible is full of passages of scripture on which to meditate. Again, for me the 23rd Psalm provides comfort and assurance:

> The LORD is my shepherd, I shall not want.
> He makes me lie down in green pastures,
> He leads me beside quiet waters,
> He restores my soul.
> He guides me in paths of righteousness
> for His name's sake.
> Even though I walk
> through the valley of the shadow of death,
> I will fear no evil,
> for You are with me;
> Your rod and your staff,
> they comfort me. (Psalm 23:1-4, NASB)

Ginny Owens sings a beautiful version of this psalm in her song "If You Want Me To." When Dick and I addressed a hospice gathering last year, I played this song for our audience. Here's an excerpt from the song:

> The pathway is broken
> And the signs are unclear
> And I don't know the reason why You brought me here
> But just because You love me the way that You do
> I'm gonna walk through the valley
> If You want me to.[2]

The transparent truth in the lyrics sung by this gifted artist touched that audience. Then, after a quiet moment, I said, " 'I'm gonna walk through the valley if You want me to.' The valley of death. You never really think about the valley of death. But when you have cancer, you think about that valley a lot. You travel down those waters. When I visit my cancer patients at the hospital, I've seen them skirt the valley of death. Sometimes they come out on the other side and live many more years. They come out on the mountain a different person because they've walked that road alone, without family or friends. But I've also been in ICU rooms when they're in the valley of death, and they pass through that valley."

Looking back on my "bubble" dream, I think I was skirting the valley of death. I was alone, unable to reach my husband and my family. I cried out but they couldn't hear me. As I think about that now, I wonder if that's what it's like in the valley of death. Of course, I wasn't really alone. God was with me, even though I wasn't aware of it then.

God is always with us. His word is filled with His promises.

So do not fear, for I am with you; do not be dismayed, for I am your God. I will strengthen you and help you; I will uphold you with my righteous right hand. (Isaiah 41:10)

Perfect love drives out fear. (1 John 4:18)

For God has not given us a spirit of fear, but of power and of love and of a sound mind. (2 Timothy 1:7, NKJV)

It's so important not to dismiss the fears your friend or loved one is experiencing as she walks this cancer path. It's like those old horror movies where the person slams the door on the scary monster only to have it reappear somewhere else in the spooky house. If a cancer patient can't express her fears, she starts stuffing it inside, but it will just surface elsewhere. She can't close the door on her fears.

The same thing goes for the patient's children, family, and caregivers. They can't close the door on their fears either. They can't live in adaptive fear forever. Adaptive fear is an emotional response that keeps you from experiencing the heightened depth and range of feelings that need to be dealt with. Many people live in adaptive denial. They stuff their fears and feelings into that box we talked about, then set it on a shelf to be carefully avoided. But life won't let you do this forever.

As for my own journey of faith through cancer, I have to admit that I never once thought, *Oh, well, God will handle this. He's in control. Nothing to worry about, so I'll just rest in His arms!* So many people say that, but not me. Not once. I was scared! What I knew about cancer scared me. Yes, deep in my heart I'd always been a person of faith, but I had to work hard at my faith when this happened. I never had problems with believing in God, but faith was a different story. My doubts were real!

Through my experiences in counseling others with cancer, I'd seen so much hurt and despondency and anger. I'd seen so much real life, when people acted horribly to each other. And it often caused me to wonder, *Where is God in all this pain and suffering?* And I struggled with the problem of evil. I questioned His purpose in all these situations. Why, God? To be perfectly honest, I have struggled with doubts like these my entire life.

But God has shown Himself to be real. Sometimes in the simplest things in my life, I've been able to trace God's hand. I'd had such a horrible year—the wreck totaling my car and injuring my neck and back, the loss of my job, and my diagnosis of breast cancer. But the day after my last radiation treatment, my final cancer treatment, I got a call for a job interview. Who could have dreamed I'd be offered a job on that specific day?

As I look back, I can see God's hand through all of it. Physically I could not have worked while undergoing chemo. Yet after the loss of my job I was given a severance package that helped to pay the bills. Later, I was able to collect unemployment. Granted, if I'd still been working, I could have taken a leave of absence guaranteed by the Family Medical Leave Act, but I would not have been paid for that time off. Who else but God could have worked that all out for good?

Throughout my life, I've seen God's hand. But there have also been times when I thought, *Lord, you need to do this and this,* and He didn't do it. I'd get angry, not understanding. As I get older, I notice I'm mellowing out more. I don't get as angry as I used to. But I still struggle.

In the Bible 1 Kings 18 and 19 tell the story of the prophet Elijah. After Elijah turned his people back to God and wiped out all the false prophets of Baal, the king's evil wife Jezebel wanted Elijah's head on a platter. After all the good he'd done and now this! Elijah feared for his life and ran and hid in a cave. "I've had enough, Lord. Please let just let me die!"

I've often done that. I've run back into the cave and cried out to God, "I don't want to do this anymore! I don't want to deal with life anymore! I don't like this! I don't like what You've given me! I can't handle it anymore!"

Those feelings were so real to me at the time. Yes, I know God is with me in that cave, but I don't always feel His presence there.

Especially in those times when I felt so bad physically and I was hurting. I felt so alone.

Even Jesus experienced that loneliness when He cried out on the cross, "My God, my God, why hast thou forsaken me?" (Matthew 27:46, KJV)

While chemo was my greatest suffering, the double mastectomy was my greatest pain. Oh, how it hurt. The tightness of those fifty stitches across my chest was unbearable. I'm allergic to almost every pain medication there is. When the pain would get so bad, I would cry out, "Please, God! Stop the pain! I've already been through so much. Why do I have to hurt this much?"

But sometimes God is silent. Sometimes He allows us to hurt. Sometimes He allows us to walk through the valley of death.

And sometimes there are no church bells ringing.

Chapter 12

I BELIEVE . . .

—Dick

I have always disliked hospital visitation. When I worked in church ministry, it was one of the requirements. Staff members had to visit the sick and those among the congregation having surgery. Most of the time this duty was divided up between the staff—I would visit one day, the music minister would visit another, and so on.

There were many reasons I disliked it. Some were because of the smells, sounds, and sights I will mention below. There was another reason, and it sounds so non-ministerial: It was inconvenient. I would have rather stayed in my office doing the work of the ministry. Writing curriculum and preparing Bible studies was much more fun than getting out into traffic. Still, the smells and sounds made me avoid these required visits like the plague. No pun intended.

Some hospitals smell like urine. Maybe this impression is psychological. Regardless, it seems that way to me. Why wouldn't it? With catheters, bed pans, accidents, soiled sheets, and spillage, maybe it is true . . . in some of them. Urine happens.

Hospital food has a peculiar smell that is uninviting to me as well. In fact, it all smells alike. Jell-O, some kind of meat, hot soup, and mashed potatoes served in hospitals does not smell or taste like Mama made it.

I don't like the sounds either. I find the moaning and groaning and calls for help disturbing. The sounds of alarms and the announcements of "STAT" while you hear the urgent footsteps of nurses and doctors running down the hall and monitors screaming from some nearby room—it's all extremely unpleasant.

But the worst offender has to be the sound of suction. It's unmistakable. Something is being sucked out of someone and into something else. My stomach turns as I imagine various liquids and wet bodily debris flowing through a hose and into a bag. Where do these bags go? I would rather not know.

The sights affect me also. I don't like to see medical apparatus, sharp gadgets, needles, IVs, heart monitors, and most especially blood.

As a child, I loved horror movies (and still do). The more bloodsucking, bloodletting, and gore the better. I paid good money to see mutilated flesh, dismemberments, and vampire bites. In my early days of black-and-white television, blood always looked black. Those effects were pitiful by today's standards. Then I graduated to movies like *Hostel*, *Saw*, and *House of a Thousand Corpses* in all their cinematic redness. When movies borderline on making you sick, they have succeeded. I give them two thumbs up.

But reality is different. The sight of real blood sends shivers down my spine. When I enter a room where someone has had surgery, often a clear plastic bag is present. This bag is attached to a tube, and the tube is going inside the person's body. The blood coming out always appears dark and thick. I am going to stop as I can't continue. Feeling a little queasy here . . .

But if I am to be completely honest, the main reason I dislike hospital visitation is because I feel so helpless and sorry for the person who is sick. Patients may be there because of injuries from a car wreck or a broken leg from falling off a ladder while trying to brush that last inch of paint on the edge of their house thirty feet in the air. If only they'd moved the ladder over a bit. Perhaps other ailments brought them here—a heart attack, pneumonia (there goes the suction sound), infections, and yes, cancer.

I remember when I was serving a church in Knoxville, Tennessee. One of our church members was diagnosed with cancer and admitted to the Baptist Hospital nearby. On my day to visit, when I entered Raymond's room, he was lying alone, flat on his back without a pillow. I supposed it had something to do with his particular kind of cancer surgery. He looked very uncomfortable.

Raymond used to be an active member of our church, but he no longer attended worship services or Sunday school regularly. He didn't tithe. He didn't volunteer in the preschool or go out on church visitation. He didn't sing in the choir or attend the Wednesday night fellowship meal and Bible study. I have heard that in some churches inactive members may not get the same attention as active ones. I may be making sweeping generalizations. I'm sure your church does not do this kind of thing or demonstrate this type of attitude.

At many seminaries and Bible colleges there are no classes on what to say or do during a hospital visit or when visiting sick people in general. When a minister visits a sick person, he is on his own. He may have observed others doing visitation and might even copy what they said or did. However, his visit is unique to his personality and theology.

The more you do it, the more familiar it becomes. The key elements of what you say start to become a litany. You say similar things on every visit. You begin to think the litany works with any kind of disease or illness. In fact, sometimes on my visits, I had no clue what the person's diagnosis or injury was. In most cases, our church secretary provided me with an official visitation request form that gave me a few details. But it didn't matter too much, because I was basically going to say the same things. If the person was conscious, here is what I included.

- A short greeting or introduction or reintroduction of myself.
- A compassionate how-are-you-doing statement.
- Let them know that the church family is praying.
- If family members are present, tell them the same things.
- A can-we-do-anything-for-you statement.
- Share a scripture verse or two.
- Offer a prayer for healing, peace, guidance, wisdom for the doctors and that the medicine would work, God's presence, and for God's will to be done.
- A quick exit (for me anyway!).

Now don't misunderstand me. This was not meaningless for me or them. I meant it, and they appreciated it. For years I have received gracious notes and cards from people I visited while serving different churches. But sometimes it felt perfunctory, mechanical, and predictable.

The visit with Raymond was particularly significant and would forever change my perspective. As I mentioned earlier, the first time I arrived in his hospital room, he was lying alone, flat on his back without a pillow.

I gave him the litany.

A week later, it was my turn to visit. . . . . He was lying alone, flat on his back without a pillow.

And I gave him the litany again.

A week later, it was my turn to visit. There was no visitation form for him. He had passed away, and I didn't even know it.

I thought about my visits to him. I had visited hundreds of sick people before. But this one stuck in my mind. I reflected on my litany. I remembered the prayers I had prayed and the Scripture promises I had read to him out of the Bible. But he had died alone . . . lying flat on his back without a pillow.

I wondered about the litany. When he was alive, how did he feel about what I said? What I didn't say? Did he even remember my visits?

I am somewhat of a theologian. I'm also very pragmatic. I deal with both faith and reality. Sometimes these two collide in a violent explosion. When they do, it can become perplexing and terribly uncomfortable.

This is nothing new to me. There are questions and issues we all struggle with, and in some cases there are no easy answers. Sometimes there seem to be no answers at all. I have dealt with these questions and issues all my life.

This particular series of visits with Raymond hit me hard. It was as if I plummeted from faith to reality. I wasn't expecting it. And I don't know why this visit prompted such a reaction. But I became acutely aware that he had died. He had passed away regardless and unrelated to my previous visits.

If I had visited him a thousand times prior and performed my litany, he still would have died unless there is a magic number of required visits that add up to a healing. I realized that my specific prayers for healing must not have worked, unless death is a form of healing. I am sure sometimes it is. But I didn't pray for that kind of healing. I prayed for Raymond to be healed physically, to eventually rise from his bed and go back home to enjoy life. I prayed for the medicine to work, but the medicine didn't work, nor did the doctor's wisdom heal him.

I came to the conclusion that God must have wanted him to die, or at least allowed him to die. It appeared that He chose to answer no to my prayer for Raymond's healing.

The Bible does teach that all are appointed to die. We all will and do. But I have prayed for complete healing hundreds of times for people not as sick as this man was, and they died too. Thousands upon thousands of other ministers have prayed for sick people to be healed, yet they died too. Many responses from God seem to be no again and again.

As a minister, in my studies on prayer, most books teach that God answers all prayers. He will answer yes, no, maybe, or wait. This, of course, assumes that God does hear us and responds when we pray. If we trust His sovereignty and wisdom, we have to accept how He responds, period.

But I thought about Raymond lying alone on his back without a pillow. What if I had told him right after I prayed for healing, that God's answer may be no, and He had answered my prayers that way thousands of times? That would not be what I would have wanted to hear.

When I visited Raymond, it was easy to see that he was feeling badly. It is said that the eyes are the window to the soul. In Raymond's case, I was looking directly into a window of suffering. There was no glare or curtains to veil his misery. A small bead of tear accumulated in the corner of his eyes and always stayed there. I imagine that the tear, like Raymond, was just too weak to move. Yes, he was suffering.

The Bible deals with many reasons for suffering, including:

- our own sin and sinful choices;
- God uses suffering to get our attention;
- suffering can make us stronger believers;
- the sins of others cause bad or harmful things to happen to us;
- a reason only God understands and we will not know in this life;
- it is just the way life is, and no explanation is needed.

In Raymond's case as in many others, I had no clue why he suffered.

As usual, I would use the standard litany: A prayer for healing, peace, guidance, wisdom for the doctors, and that the medicine would work, God's presence, and for God's will to be done. When I prayed for him, was he trusting that my prayers for healing would work? How did he feel about those prayers as he was getting sicker and sicker? How did that affect the way he may have viewed God and His will?

Sometimes, as a minister, I cannot be honest. I cannot express any questions about issues like this. I am supposed to be the example of unwavering faith for others to follow. I am supposed to give a response that represents God.

When believers look up at me from a sick bed, experiencing all sorts of agony and pain, they look to me for answers. I try. I pray and ask for God's healing, but they may die. Or I pray for God's presence, when it feels that He is not there. I pray the pain would lessen, even as morphine does not take it away. I pray for perfect peace, and I still see the fear in the person's eyes. I try so hard.

Here is a prayer I have prayed so many times by the bed of someone who is sick.

> Dear God, thank You for loving us and for Your presence in the midst of our pain. I lift _____ up to You and ask You to be with him in a very special way. I pray that You would touch _____ and heal his body. Whether it is by Your divine touch or through the miracle of medicine, I pray for wholeness and health and that Your will may be done. Thank You, Lord, for hearing our prayers. Amen.

Sometimes they make it home. Sometimes they don't. I have to be honest. Many times, I have left their bedsides and never thought about the ramifications of how my prayer may have affected them or their family later.

I pray for God's will to be done, but I have wondered what suffering people think about that. As they look death squarely in the eye, is this comforting to them? Do they wonder if it is God's will for them to be healed or to die? I would opt for healing every time. Sometimes there is only one way to know for sure—if they die or not.

When things seem to get worse and unanswerable questions about suffering come up, sometimes all we can say is that God's ways are not our ways. Sometimes that answer seems like faith's last resort. Is it enough? Is it possible some sick people feel it would be more comforting to know His ways now? Would I?

But for Christian believers, we give them the great hope and blessing of going to heaven. This is a great comfort. But some people are not ready to get on the next trainload out of here, nor are their family members.

Then I wonder about sick people who do not believe in God. Many believers pray at their bedsides as well and seek to share a particular system of beliefs with them. Some people believe that if the patient rejects their "religion" or theology, they will be forever punished. They not only suffer here, they die and continue to suffer in the afterlife. This must be absolutely heartbreaking for the ones sharing, not to mention the one dying.

Reader, I hope that these confessions do not shock you or make you feel that I have not tried to be the best possible minister I can be. But I am human and not a superman. I would be lying if I didn't tell you that I struggle.

And I have reasons for sharing these confessions.

When Deb was diagnosed with cancer, it became very personal. It was not someone else crying on my shoulder and scared she may be dying. It was my wife in pain. She was the one lying in bed because the poisonous chemicals pumped through her body made her so sick she could not get up. She was the one I cried about every morning while driving to work after kissing her bald little head when I said good-bye.

This was my children's mom. I knew she wondered about her legacy. *Was I a good mom? Have I prepared my kids for the future? Am I even going be a part of it? Will I be here for their weddings and graduations? Will I get to know my grandchildren?*

She also became concerned about me. *How would Dick react without me? Could he even live without me? How could he ever say good-bye to me? How could I say good-bye to him?*

Deb was also an oncology counselor for eighteen years, knowing step by step what her cancer could do. She was a professional health care provider who had seen hundreds of cancer patients not last a year with a type of cancer nowhere nearly as bad as hers.

I could never use a litany with Deb. The questions I pondered previously became more intensified for me. The unanswerable questions became a plague, like locusts devouring entire landscapes. I felt as if I were falling off a precipice with no rope and no one to help me as I screamed, "Falling!"

What if I pray for healing, but she dies? What if I pray for peace and see the fear in her eyes? What if I pray for the doctors and medications to work, and the cancer returns violently in six months? How could I possibly pray for God's will to be done if that ends in her death? Should I beg God? And for how long? Is there a certain number of people I need to enlist to pray for her before she is healed? Is there a quota?

Frankly, I started being scared to pray because I didn't want her to be disappointed if God didn't answer my prayers. I didn't want to be disappointed either.

I asked and still ask so many questions: *Why her? Why now? Why me?* But eventually it all settled to *Why her?* She is the nicest person in the world. She has done nothing horribly wrong to deserve this. Would "deserving" even be a good enough reason for getting cancer anyway? Again there are no easy answers.

My life became more dual: two persons living in the same body. I was the minister on the outside—someone expected to console, provide hope, answers, and assurance. But the other part of me remained in darkness, like some secret sin, wondering if God even knew about Deb or cared.

The latter was winning.

I know and love hundreds of Christians and ministers. They are some of the most wonderful people I know. They are sincere, caring, and concerned. They tell me the following.

"We are praying for her and God's healing."

"I believe in prayer."

"God healed my wife when she went through the same thing."

"Trust God through this."

"God will keep you in perfect peace."

"There is a reason for this, and we may not know it now."

"We are praying. We are praying. We are praying . . . "

Again, "How's Debbie?"

And "How are you holding up?"

And "Is there anything I can do for you?"

Some sounded like a litany.

I heard this hundreds of times. Sometimes I wanted to scream at them: "Yes, you can do something for me . . . *shut up*! I don't want to hear this right now! I don't want to give you a play-by-play account or hear your platitudes. Don't tell me that you are praying for Deb or that you believe in prayer, insinuating that healing is only one prayer away. I am so afraid your prayers will not work! Don't talk to me about being in the center of God's will! If this is it, *I don't want to be there.*"

Instead, I say: "Deb is devastated, and so am I."

I want to continue, "Where is God in all of this? Why doesn't God hear your prayers or mine? Why does she not miraculously get healed? What possible good can come out of this? How could a loving God allow this to happen?"

But I bite my tongue and say nothing more. Like millions who have bit their tongues all throughout human history.

Is this normal? I think it is. Some may not think so. I don't want to talk to them.

I want so much to rest in simple theological rhymes and reasons. Deep down inside I want to hold on and believe their wonderful words of encouragement, help, and hope. I want to believe and accept what I myself have told others many times.

There are some things on this side of eternity we do not understand.

God will keep you in perfect peace.

There is a reason for this.

We will keep praying and asking God for healing.

His grace is sufficient.

But each time I heard statements like these, my heart sank. I wondered what was wrong with me.

They were trying to help and show genuine concern. I had to appreciate that. I would respond and say, "Amen. Thank you so much. This means a lot to me." I had to respond like a minister. For me, this was difficult. But I hide my real feelings well. I'm sure they hide theirs too from time to time.

Then I began to feel guilty and scared. *What if God gets mad at me for asking questions or feeling this way? Will He allow Deb to get worse? Is He going to punish me by allowing her to die? Will He not heal Deb now? Have I blown it with God? Don't I have any faith?*

I felt as if her healing was dependent upon me and my faith. My faith was too weak. How could I make it stronger?

Some said that God may be trying to get my attention through Deb's cancer. Honestly, this was very disturbing to me. I could not believe God would use the suffering of my wife just to get to me . . . to teach me a lesson or something. Use someone else. Give me a dose of Job: boils, sores, dust, and ashes. I will listen, I promise. Just leave Deb alone.

Perhaps the most difficult part of this is being a spiritual encouragement to Deb. I don't want to share these hard questions with her. I can't. She needs me to be strong. She needs me to pray, believe, hope, and be her strength. Sometimes I am. But sometimes I can't, and she understands. And this is why I love her with all my heart. She becomes my strength. She prays for me, believes, and hopes when I can't do it for her.

I am so thankful that in her chapter "Fear, Faith, and Cancer" Deb speaks of the simple faith that has given her sustenance each day as she battles this disease. Even in the midst of uncertainties about the "why" questions, she still finds solace. This is such an inspiration to me. If I were in the same situation as Deb, could I find such solace? In the midst of human suffering, the peace of God is there. It's available. I've taught this truth to hundreds of others over the years. But sometimes the ones who know about it best are the last to put it into practice. I guess it's akin to "Those who can't do, teach!"

As you should know by now, I love Deb with all my heart. She is the most precious gift I have or will ever have in my entire human existence. As the ordained minister, I should have been the one writing that chapter, expressing such simple faith. You may be wondering why I didn't and instead wrote this one.

The truth is it's easy for me to speak of simple faith when it's a person I barely know lying on his back without a pillow. But when the one I love and cherish the most is facing total uncertainty about tomorrow, it's hard for me to "just let go and leave it to God." I want to fix it and make it right. I want to protect her from all harm. I want guarantees that everything will be okay and Deb will outlive me. Only then do I recognize that it is totally and undeniably out of my hands, and I have to learn to live with it.

One of the most honest discourses in the New Testament is found in Mark 9. It is the story of a dad bringing his sick son to Jesus to be healed. His heart is broken. The man asks Jesus to take pity and to help his son if He can. Jesus says that everything is possible for the person who believes. Then the man responds, "I do believe; help me overcome my unbelief."

His son is healed.

Jesus says in Matthew 17:20 that if a person has faith as small as a mustard seed, he can tell a mountain to move and it will move. Nothing will be impossible.

Cancer is that mountain. It is in our way. Right now it is not moving. I am willing to go around it, over it, under it, or through it. We want it to be far behind us, only a faint outline appearing in the distant past as we walk hand in hand through greener pastures.

So where am I at the time of this writing?

I am hoping that God is not mad at me for asking difficult questions.

I am devastated.

I am praying.

I am asking God for total healing, and that the cancer will never come back.

I am praying for God to guide the doctors and for the medicines to work.

I am looking for a mustard seed.

I have come to realize and reaffirm that I am totally helpless. There is nowhere else I can go, nothing else I can do, and no one else I can run to but God.

I am crying unto heaven, "Lord I believe! Help me when it is too hard to believe."

This must be the simple faith I crave.

It is not just a litany.

Chapter 13

HOW TO BE A FRIEND TO A FRIEND WHO HAS CANCER

—Deb

God never loved me in so sweet a way before
'Tis He alone who can such blessings send.
And when His love would new expressions find,
He brought you to me and said, "Behold, a friend."
Author Unknown

I remember a weekend away with my YaYa sisters when I gave them a calligraphy print of this verse to show them how special they are to me. Our YaYa group began more than twenty-five years ago when we all lived in the Clearwater, Florida, area. We call ourselves the "Sistahs" since we thought YaYa was overworked and oversold.

We all had connections with First Baptist Church of Indian Rocks. Our children were similar in ages and grew up going to the same schools and playing the same sports. Over the next twenty-five years, our jobs or spouses separated us geographically but never spiritually, and with the modern era of cell phones, never logistically. As a matter of fact, we became closer as we continued to get together at the beach or in cabins located halfway from each of us.

Trying to make this journey at least once and maybe twice a year, we would share our innermost secrets, our blessings, our trials, what we thought our husbands should do better, and, of course, all about our children. We would raise each other up, and sometimes "positively and graciously" critique each other when the need arose. We know each of us is there for the others. When one of our spouses died, we immediately dropped everything and hastened to our dear friend's side. When one of us had a diagnosis of cancer, we stayed in constant touch with affirmations, cards, and visits, both personally and by phone.

They are my friends. They are my soul mates.

They strengthened me with constant prayers in my darkest hours. Sometimes I didn't feel like talking to them, but they understood. They still understand today when I feel tired or just sick of it all. They understand when I don't want to talk about cancer for once and just want to talk about politics, or the loves of our children, or nothing more than the weather.

We have a connection that some people find hard to relate to. It is a spiritual, *phileo*, and affirming type of love. We are lucky, because there are many people who go through life without one friend. I have seen this phenomenon over the years as I have sat on the other side of the couch. So I feel very lucky and blessed.

As a counselor for oncology patients, sometimes I am that missing link of friendship for them. The nurses and staff in the physicians' offices are cognizant of this also and often search out those poor souls who are alone because it is crucial for a cancer patient to have a support circle of *someone*. Most of us do have some family and friends to support us.

The rollercoaster ride of cancer has so many ups and downs and twists and turns that it's difficult to hang on and stay in your seat. When you are first diagnosed with cancer, people may come from every direction, asking the same questions over and over again. You think that if you have to explain it to one more person, you'll scream! I always suggest that my patients have one key contact person who can relay all the information to others or use a Web site such as CaringBridge.org to disseminate information in a timely and sympathetic method. This protects your time and sanity.

Many people may withdraw from you. This can hurt. People are usually afraid of the situation, and they are very self-critical. They don't know what to say, so they solve this inadequacy by not saying anything or by not coming to visit at all. It is much the same as when someone dies. People may call or stop by once to bring a casserole, then they withdraw into anonymity. Usually it's not because they don't care. They just don't know what to do.

From my perspective as a counselor and now as a patient, here are some suggestions on how to be a friend to a friend who has cancer.

1. Make contact with your friend often and simply be there for her. Maintain a loving, reassuring presence and don't always have a deep theological sermon for her. Sometimes a short visit or a simple phone call is all she needs. Let her guide you. Look for clues or just ask her what she needs. Patients are usually not very hard to please. One time I asked one of my visitors if she could take out my dogs for me. This is no small task as I have three dogs including one that weighs 100 pounds. This was a huge favor. A simple card, a flower, a dinner are all valuable. I am never hard to please.

2. Maintain a calm focus for the visit. Please don't come over and dump all your most recent problems about that guy you met at your sister's party. Be understanding and intuitive. Do talk about everyday events that may make me laugh or smile. I still like those stupid blonde jokes because I've been hearing them for fifty-five years! Tell me about the movie you just saw or what's happening on your favorite TV show.

3. Try not to say, "Call me if you need anything." Be more specific and helpful. If you have a child who goes to the same school as mine, ask if you could do the driving. Or if you take your kids to the movies, invite my kid too. These types of specific offers tell me you want to be involved. Look for things that need to be done. As I said before, be intuitive. If you notice the lawn hasn't been mowed in weeks, don't report it to the neighborhood association. Offer to mow the lawn (or at least make your husband do it). These are the acts of service that make someone feel loved and valued.

4. It's okay to ask how your friend feels or what is happening with the treatment. The reality of cancer is always there, ever lurking with its tests, blood work, and x-rays. It is the proverbial elephant in the room that's not going away. Don't be afraid of tears because they may come. Let your friend cry, laugh, scream, or just talk. Take the cues from her. Remember you are there to serve her.

5. Understand that it may be hard to ask for help. It is very hard for me to ask for help. I've always been the caregiver in my home and in my job. I notice the sadness or joy in other people's eyes or I hear it in their voices. I try to forget that I don't feel well as I try to do all the things I used to do—cook, clean, go to the bank, go to the grocery store and the dry cleaners. I'm the one who always notices that the

dog dish is empty. I'm the one who notices the hair bunnies on the floor. And, yes, I even notice when all the dogs have been scratching at the door waiting to go outside for the past half hour. I loved when my sisters-in-law would come to visit. They didn't ask me what needed to be done—they did it! They noticed everything. I didn't have to ask a thing. It felt wonderful.

6. Provide encouragement for the family also. My husband carried a huge burden. I know he confided in others and asked for their help. It was very important to me that he had his own resources. I worried about my children also. They needed reassurance, and I had always been the one to stand in the gap. I was the one they confided in. But now they didn't want to burden me, and they were scared. Listen to them for me. Answer their questions. They have their unique fears and pain also.

7. Be available for crisis situations. Surgery and the beginning of chemotherapy or radiation are all difficult times for patients and their caregivers. These are days to bring food. Give them a choice about what to bring. I know my tastes changed, which was completely normal, so there were things I couldn't eat. For some reason I loved banana Popsicles and grape juice. These were not high in nutritional value, but they were comforting to me. Knowing my family was going to eat a good meal, however, made me feel better even though I couldn't join them.

8. Discuss the situation with the patient and his family with an attitude of realistic hope. For instance, don't start talking about his will on the day of his diagnosis. Cancer is almost considered a chronic disease now. Moreover, oncologists hesitate to use the word cured anymore. They prefer to talk in terms of "today" to the patient and his family: "Today there are no indications that you have cancer." This is a more realistic statement because we know that all too often cancer returns.

Sometimes specific information can be extremely encouraging for patients and their families, such as these findings from the National Cancer Institute's 2008 Annual Report. "A new report from the nation's leading cancer organizations shows that, for the first time since the report was first issued in 1998, both incidence and death rates for all cancers combined are decreasing for both men and women, driven largely by declines in some of the most common types of cancer."[1]

But if circumstances take a turn for the worst, meet the family at the point of their need. Remember to listen, listen, and then listen some more. More often than not, they will know the reality of their situation and appreciate both your presence and the gift of time.

Oh, by the way, did I mention you should listen?

9. Touch the patient. I loved it when someone would scratch my back. Just for a few moments I would feel loved. The power of touch is so meaningful. Jesus physically touched most of those He healed. When I visited in the hospital or in the infusion areas, I usually touched my patients in some way to reassure them, sometimes nothing more than a toe squeeze or a pat on the back. Cancer is not contagious, though some people still believe that myth. So don't forget the power of personal touch. Oftentimes, if Dick would just lie beside me and hold my hand or arm, my breathing would return to normal and my anxiety would lessen. I felt wrapped in his love and concern. These were powerful moments in my recovery process.

10. Finally, remember the Golden Rule: Do unto others as you would have them do unto you. Think about what would make you feel good. Think about what needs could be met that would help if ^ were the patient.

11. Above all, don't abandon your friend. Just love her.

Chapter 14

WHAT NOT TO SAY

—Dick

I don't know what to say about this subject or how to say it without hurting someone's feelings. Many wonderful people have shown expressions of concern for Deb and me in different ways. Some have been funny and others depressing. Some have been right on the mark and helpful at a particular moment. Still others have ticked me off so badly I had to run away before I killed someone.

I have read body language, evaluated tones of voices, overly analyzed, and scrutinized every well-intentioned word and sentence. Why? Because I am so broken by what Deb is going through. I am angry. I am judgmental. With all the disappointments we've received from doctor visits and tests, I am at my wit's end.

At times I feel like I'm hanging by a thin thread of sanity, and the thread is unraveling. I am nervous, tired, anxious, hyper, depressed, and confused. I want to run away and hide. I want to disappear. I don't want to be around people. I want to stay in my room and be alone. But then Deb brings me back to reality.

"Dick, you have always been like this!"

Okay. I confess. She's right. I was a Type A, melancholy, overly analytical, somewhat cynical, psychotic, neurotic, and suspicious guy before she had cancer. But since her diagnosis, I've become worse!

Deb's cancer brings out the best and the worst in me. I have become very sensitive to every aspect of the disease. As I said before, show me a cancer awareness commercial on television and I get mad. I hate pink ribbons. I despise hearing about recurrences. I am sick and tired of people dying of it. It just makes me want to cuss. Sometimes I do.

The Bible talks about the power of the tongue to lash out and to destroy if used incorrectly. Most people have been hurt by it. Many times it is used for good; other times it's used as a dangerous weapon. It can summon up old memories. Almost everyone can remember a time in grammar school when a careless comment or word wounded them and how it still bothers them today.

The tongue also has the power to soothe. Kind words, joyful singing, elegant poetry, and the most beautiful expression of all, "I love you," emanate from it.

The tongue can also communicate stupid thoughts, ideas, and sayings. It can be a faux pas machine. It can be stepped upon, swallowed, stuck out, and bit. But holding it back is far more difficult.

Here is a pathetic personal example. I have said some idiotic things in my life, many I regret. A remark about Deb's hair stands out above them all. She still remembers it and brings it up from time to time.

During our first year of marriage Deb had long hair, not shoulder-length but mid-neck. One time when she returned from a salon visit, only upper-ear length remained. I experienced both shock and amazement. I loved her long hair and could not believe that she left part of it on a stylist's floor to be swept up and discarded. In a snippy and uncaring manner, I dropped a fierce tongue bomb: "You cannot possibly think that looks good."

Wrong thing to say. Wish I'd never said it. She cried and cried.

When I tell that story, I get boos and horrified looks from the women in the audience. Husbands are totally shocked and avoid eye contact with their wives. Who knows, maybe they have said something similar or even worse, and I've reminded their wives of it just to take the focus off me. The women hate me afterward and rightly so. I am an idiot. And I still apologize to Deb for saying it.

I love Deb so much, and I hope that's been obvious throughout all my chapters. But over the years, a few of her questions have put me in quite precarious situations. At times I didn't know what to say or do.

To make my point, let me share with you two specific questions Deb has asked me. I would not consider these tongue bombs, but rather tongue tasers. Police tasers typically hit a person with 50,000 volts, then drop to around 1200. Tasers disrupt a body's ability to communicate with its muscles, making the person collapse to the floor. Deb's tongue tasers came in the form of questions that disrupted my ability to communicate with her. When I collapsed, I wished I could stay on the floor.

During one of our holiday meals, Deb asked, "Does this broccoli casserole taste okay to you? It tastes funny to me."

Perhaps a word of background is in order. Deb always prides herself on her broccoli casserole recipe. She must have gotten it from her great, great, great-grandmother. It may have been originally written on the back of the Shroud of Turin. A holy recipe. The sin of blasphemy awaits anyone who speaks against it. It is a place where no forgiveness exists.

She serves this dish on all special occasions: Christmas, Thanksgiving, Easter, birthdays, Lent, Festivus, Arbor Day, Labor Day, Mother's Day, May Day, Pay Day, Today, and Any Day. This piping hot culinary masterpiece proudly sits center stage on the dining room table. It is rightly elevated on a golden trivet, towering above all other dishes. It stands majestically high, like the pyramided peak of an Aztec altar where warriors worship and sacrifices are made to appease angry gods. It lives and breathes. It has a pulse. I swear I have seen it glowing in the dark. I have witnessed tiny angelic fairies fluttering in and out of the hot steam rising as if from the mouth of a sacred volcano. High above it, Deb stands back in reverence and beams with pride like the first time she witnessed the miracle of birth.

Bottom line: Whether it's good or not good, it is always good. There are no other possibilities.

When she asked that question, if I answered yes, the conversation went like this.

"Does this broccoli casserole taste okay to you? It tastes funny to me."

"Honey, it tastes fine."

"You're lying. Tell me the truth! Does this taste funny to you?"

"Honey, it tastes fine to me—really!"

"You're lying. I can always tell when you're lying."

"I like it," I say with timidity.

"So you only *like* it?"

"No, I meant to say that I *love* it."

"Why didn't you say that in the first place? You obviously hate it. Well, just don't eat it then. I'll just throw it away! Heaven forbid I make you something you don't like. Don't worry. I'll never make it for you again."

Then she cried . . .

If I answered no, the conversation went like this.

151

"Does this broccoli casserole taste okay to you? It tastes funny to me."

"Honey, it tastes fine."

"You're lying. Tell me the truth! Does this taste funny to you?"

"Honey, it tastes fine to me . . . really."

"You're lying. I can always tell when you're lying."

"Well, yes, it does taste a little funny," I say right before I kill myself.

"Just don't eat it then," she says, "I'll just throw it away! Heaven forbid I make you sick. You never liked my broccoli casserole anyway, did you? Don't worry. I'll never make it for you again."

Then she cried . . .

Guess who cleaned up the kitchen for the next two years. The sad thing is it had absolutely nothing to do with the broccoli casserole.

Another tongue taser: As Deb finished dressing on the evening of our anniversary a few years ago, she asked, "Does this outfit make me look fat?"

Perhaps another word of background. When Deb buys a new outfit, she stands in front of the full-length mirror and moves from side to side. Then she turns halfway around and twists her hips and neck far enough to the left, and then to right, to be able to glimpse her shoulders, lower back, and other important anatomical regions.

She lightly brushes off a piece of stray lint clinging to the lapel of her new outfit. She gently pulls down at the waistline, smoothes it over her thighs, and lightly shakes her booty while still moving from side to side. She tugs at her collar and pulls down each sleeve. She leans closer to the mirror and corrects a tiny, out-of-place streak of lipstick with her fresh nail-painted pinky. She fondles her hair lovingly and blinks her eyes twice. When she does those blinks, my heart begins to sink like the Titanic. I know what is coming.

She turns around with her back to the mirror. She places her hands on her hips, bends her waist slightly to the left, sticks out her right leg, and juts out her chest slightly. She cocks her chin up a bit, and looks straight at me. She is ready. And I enter a no-win situation. We have entered the *Twilight Zone*. It's a perfect storm coming at me like an F5 tornado from hell. I begin to sweat and look up to heaven for divine intervention. *Oh, my God, . . . please help me, Jesus!*

Then she zaps me with the taser. Eight short words that have made armies of men cower and willingly surrender throughout all human history.

"Honey, does this outfit make me look fat?"

With that question suspended in the air between us, I stare at her, bewildered. But I must not be bewildered. That would show hesitancy and indecision. I can't smile because she will think I am secretly laughing at her. I can't shrug because she'll think I don't care. In fact, I can't do anything but *exist* at that moment.

I display no noticeable bodily movement. My eyes are fixed, my face muscles paralyzed. All normal human emotions cease. The only sound I hear is the ever increasing thump, thump, thump of my heart.

I seek an appropriate response that does not exist anywhere in the vast universe of space and time. Neither Albert Einstein, Carl Sagan, nor Stephen Hawkin have discovered a formula or theory that will work in this situation. Still, I have to settle for some response. Here are my choices.

If I say yes, she will cry.

If I say no, she won't believe me, and she will cry.

If I say, "Honey, you look fine," *fine* is bad, and she will cry.

If I say, "Honey, you are beautiful," she will think I only said that because she thinks she looks fat. Then she will cry.

If I fall dead of a heart attack, she will believe I died because she looks fat.

I have a theory. All female clothing manufacturers are women. They create their designs for the sole purpose of making women think they look fat in them. You know what? Their objective is working very well. The reason they do this? Simple. They hate men.

All kidding aside (was that kidding?), the most basic question I'm asked is, "How is Deb doing today?" It seems like a very simple question to answer, but often it is not.

I generally find there is not enough time to answer that question with the answer it deserves. It's a serious question with the potential for a very long and emotional reply. The answer may include tears, a quivering voice, and deep, sighing sobs. Sometimes the person asking doesn't really want to hear the answer anyway, especially if the answer is accompanied by tears and sobs.

So my usual response is "She's doing okay." I say this with a sense of untruthfulness because with cancer, I don't think anyone really does okay. The other person usually replies with an enthusiastic "Great!" As if everything really is okay. And most often "great" is the end of the conversation. After that, what else can I say?

Now, if I am truthful, I would say things like "She was so scared last night about dying that all we could do was to hold each other and cry like babies." Or "She spent yesterday lying on her back hoping she wouldn't start throwing up again."

On some of my darker days, I've answered with these more honest responses. Typically the person just stares at me, like a deer in the headlights. The tension and discomfort is palpable. I try to hide my emotions, but sometimes they come out unexpectedly. When that happens, I always feel the need to apologize for my honesty. I feel guilty for sharing my pain with them.

Advice is something I don't need from casual well wishers. Here are a few words of wisdom I've actually been told . . . with just a bit of embellishment, of course.

"Does she take vitamins? I heard of a lady who took one vitamin a day, and her cancer went away in one month."

Wow, let me get a bottle of those chewable vitamins that look like dinosaurs! I wonder if the American Cancer Society knows this. Think of all that money spent on research when a cancer patient can get cured simply by nibbling on the head of a T-Rex!

"Has she tried exercise and a proper diet? I heard of a lady who had cancer and cured herself in one month by getting the right exercise and eating the right foods."

I wonder if Deb's oncologist knows this. I'm going to get Deb to do a hundred jumping jacks and eat a pound of dandelion greens each night as soon as she finishes throwing her guts up after her most recent chemotherapy.

"Does she maintain a positive mental attitude? I heard of a lady who had cancer and cured herself in one month by avoiding negative thinking and maintaining a positive mental attitude."

Thanks! I cannot wait to tell Deb! I'm going to get all the positive mental attitude books I can find for her to read, just a soon as she feels well enough to read. Right now she can barely move her head from side to side. And I might need to wait until she stops crying.

"There are natural cures they don't want to tell you about. I heard of a lady who had cancer and cured herself in one month by discovering the miracle cure doctors don't want you to know."

Sadly, Barnes and Noble sold out of it as well as Borders. I asked Deb's oncologist if he knew of a miracle cure. He said he did but wouldn't tell me.

Deb has received many wonderful cards and notes from friends and family. It means so much to us that others are thinking about her and praying for her. But she has also received some cards from complete strangers who have heard about her illness from others. One of the cards we received in the mail stands out among all the others. It originated from a "prayer warrior" in a local church. Many churches have prayer ministries with a prayer room, where church members go to pray over needs and requests that are sent in. Sometimes they write notes of encouragement and mail them to the ones they have prayed for. Recently she received one of these.

As I closed the mailbox, I had no clue who had sent the card. Deb's name and medical condition had been forwarded by a friend to her church's prayer ministry. Only the name and address of the church appeared as a return address. Deb opened the envelope and laughed. She read the handwritten note. "I wanted to let you know that I prayed for you today. My wife had cancer and didn't survive." Are you kidding? We laughed out loud. Even with cancer, we still have a sense of humor. It's a good thing.

On some occasions I've been asked what stage of cancer she has or did it spread to any lymph nodes. These kinds of questions are usually asked by someone who knows about the disease; either they've had it or someone they know has. When I say Stage IIIA or that the surgeon found the disease in four nodes, their countenance falls. They woefully shake their head and bite their bottom lip. They stare at me with sad eyes and say, "I'm so sorry." To me, this doesn't help. They might as well show me a pamphlet about caskets. I don't want to know they know how bad it is.

It's one thing to express concern; it's quite another to begin digging her grave.

Please understand. All of these questions, words of advice, and attempts at encouragement come from well-meaning people who are legitimately concerned. I would never respond negatively to them. And while sometimes I have to hold back my emotions while I smile and say thank you, I still appreciate their hearts.

Perhaps these questions and responses don't cause you a problem at all. A few of them may. Each of us is different, and sometimes there is no right or wrong answer. Often I have found it to be purely subjective. Frankly, most of the time I wouldn't know what to say back to me! Sometimes I need one thing, sometimes another, sometimes nothing at all. I realize people are not mind readers. Should they be, my mind would be such a jumbled mess that they couldn't decipher it anyway.

Of one thing I am sure: My heart aches so much for Deb. Whenever anyone asks me how she is doing or seeks to give me advice, I hope I convey one unwavering and eternal truth—that I love her with all my heart. In the end, this is all that matters anyway.

Chapter 15

THE CASE FOR COUNSELING

—Deb

One day, while going in for one of my treatments, I stopped by to have my blood work done. This was the same oncology office where I'd worked as a counselor before I was laid off. I saw my oncologist in the hall, the same doctor I'd worked with for more than seven years, and stopped to ask him a question.

"Dr. McCoy, I really need to speak to a good counselor. Do you know of anyone?" While my question was half tongue-in-cheek, I was also serious. I needed someone other than family members I could talk to. Someone I could open my heart to. Someone who would understand what I was feeling. Someone who understood the dynamic of cancer.

He smiled. "I know of a good one, but she's not here anymore." We shared a chuckle, but my need was real.

I may be a counselor, but I knew I needed counseling.

Cancer is unlike any other type of disease. As I've said before, it affects every aspect of your life—finances, emotions, physical abilities, work, sex, how you think, your children, spouse, family, extended family, and everyone else around you. You need someone at the point of diagnosis who knows all about cancer to guide you and help you to understand the difficult maze ahead.

Cancer is like its own country. It has its own language, culture, and way of living. When you're diagnosed, you arrive in this new country not knowing the language. You have no idea what Stage I, II, III, or IV means. You don't understand blood counts. You don't have a clue what treatments you'll encounter or how they'll make you feel. You need a tour guide, and that person is an oncology counselor.

I've had nurses who aren't trained in oncology tell me they know how to care for critically ill patients in ICU, but cancer is a new world to them. Because cancer still equals death in so many people's minds, the emotional aspect of this disease can often far outweigh the physical issues they're facing.

Dr. Bernie Siegel, author of numerous books including *Faith, Hope and Healing*, once said a positive mind-set can enable you to control your own destiny. "The power to heal comes from the human mind through will, determination, and love."[1] But as we all know, that's just not true. Such philosophies make patients feel like they've somehow failed if they're trying to stay positive but still can't beat the cancer.

We've talked about taking action to help overcome the fears of cancer. But some days, when you feel so terrible, you can't do anything. And you have to learn how to accept where you are. A counselor can help you to understand that it's okay to feel what you're feeling. He or she can tell you it's normal for you to feel this way while battling cancer.

A trained counselor can also help you to connect the dots between what you're feeling internally and what you're experiencing externally. When you're physically so sick from treatment that you can't work and do all you need to do—like caring for your family or taking care of the house—internally you're screaming for help, but you may not know how to ask for it.

A wife who's fighting cancer may not want to ask her husband for more help around the house because it makes her feel like she's failing, no longer capable and successful like she used to be. Some people feel that they're less of a person than they used to be. *Cancer has changed who I am. I want to go back to what I used to be.* A good counselor can help you to work through those inner and outer struggles, the inner angst that's going against what's happening on the outside.

A counselor can help you to redefine your life and your purpose in life. Some people are not able to go back to work after cancer. Men especially, whose lives are so strongly defined by what they do for a living, may struggle with egos that can't handle their new nonworking lifestyle. It affects not only their finances, but their purposefulness in life as well. Their goals in life have to be reestablished.

In working with patients, I've learned that many of these new goals must be incrementally small. Maybe today's goal is nothing more than feeling better. Tomorrow's goal is trying to cope with the stresses of everyday life by journaling for a while.

Sometimes the changes are bigger. You may have to change relationship dynamics and responsibilities. The breadwinner may have to become the stay-at-home parent. A grown child may need to become more of a parent to his parent. Family members may need to learn how to ask each other for more help. In counseling, we can help cancer patients and their caregivers learn to deal with all these changes, big or small.

Counselors offer a source of confidentiality. Things you may not be able to share with your spouse or family you can freely discuss with a counselor. Sometimes patients don't even tell their doctors how they really feel for fear of more tests or more scary diagnoses. They so desperately want to believe their doctor is succeeding in his treatment of them that they won't admit they're having problems. With a counselor, they feel more freedom to tell what's really happening to them, how they're really feeling.

On the darkest nights, if I shared with my husband about my fear of dying, he would often cry. I felt horrible for making him suffer like that. If I'd had a counselor, I could have shared from the depths of my heart how I was really feeling. Instead, my husband had to play that role. It wasn't fair for me to put him through that, and I felt guilty.

When patients come to see me, they know they're completely free to open up all their emotions. Many of them are angry—at the disease, at their doctor, at their spouse or other family members. I was a safe place for them to scream and cry and express all those emotions.

One day a woman came into my office cussing up a storm. She was the caregiver for her ailing husband, and she had to change his sheets up to ten times a day. She was exhausted. Then she learned about a special kind of plastic bed sheet that wouldn't have to be changed constantly. That one simple suggestion completely changed her ability to care for her husband and restored her emotional well-being.

Sometimes it takes so little. Through counseling, she was allowed to express her true feelings—"I'm so sick of taking care of my husband!"—and not feel threatened by saying it out loud. I was able to tell her how normal those feelings are. People get sick and tired of taking care of sick people! Hearing those simple words made all the difference for her.

A patient once told me, "This is a place where I feel safe being miserable. I can be miserable, and nobody gives me a pep talk." That's a great compliment to a counselor, but it takes time to get to that point. A relationship has to be developed to establish trust. Patients must know they'll be supported and understood. While technical people tend to look at patients as "the breast cancer in room 4" or "the prostate in room 10," counselors see patients as individuals with unique situations and unique problems. They can offer support in very practical ways— helping with drug assistance, assisting with transportation needs, buying a wig, and so on.

Counseling helps the whole family, and it's just as important for them as for the patient. For caregivers, the biggest concern is fatigue. They become utterly exhausted. I always stress the need for them to take care of themselves. I would give them permission to take a break and leave the patient in someone else's care for a while because most often those self-needs make them feel guilty.

By reinforcing their need to be refreshed—to get some sleep or get their nails done or go fishing—I can help them restore their own mental health and emotional well being. Otherwise they quickly burn out. I help them recognize the necessity of taking care of themselves, and I help them find the resources and avenues to do that.

Sometimes they just need to vent.

"He won't take his medications like the doctor instructed."

"She keeps getting up to cook all the meals instead of resting like she's supposed to."

"She won't let me help her."

Caregivers need a safe place to talk through their concerns and frustrations. They may be sad or angry or frustrated, and they need to express those feelings away from the patient. They'll come in and yell at me, and that's just what they need to do. At times I almost have to teach them what they can and cannot do. I give them permission to feel how they're feeling. I give them permission to take care of themselves: *It's okay to take a day off to get some rest. If you go out to dinner, he's not going to die. And even if he should die while you're gone, it's not your fault!* Sometimes they just need to hear it.

For cancer patients, sleep is a subject of utmost importance. Cancer changes sleep patterns. Either patients cannot sleep at all or they sleep too much. Sometimes the issue revolves around going to sleep. Patients may lie there feeling awful, experiencing pain, or fretting over their situation for hours. We would work on strategies to improve sleep habits. We would talk about their routine, limiting the naps they took during the day and making sure they went to bed at the same time every night. I'd often suggest a bath right before bed to help relax them. If they don't fall asleep after lying in bed for an hour, I urge them to get up for a while.

Without enough sleep, the fear and anxiety levels increase and the coping strategies tend to suffer. Everyone needs REM sleep (Rapid Eye Movement sleep, which indicates a deeper level of restful sleep), and for some patients that may require a sleeping aid or anti-anxiety medication.

Many of my patients are afraid of becoming addicted to any kind of sleep aid and refuse to take them. As a counselor, I am completely frustrated by this kind of response. I tell them that this is a time in their life when they have to look at things from an entirely different perspective. Pain medication is necessary to handle pain. Sleeping aids may be necessary to help them sleep better, which then helps them to cope with their disease better. Anti-anxiety medications help with anxiety.

They have to look at this time in their life unlike any other experience they've ever had. They have to learn to accept this kind of help as much as allowing someone to cook them a dinner or run errands for them. These medications recommended by their health professionals are there to help them, not to hurt them.

Is There a Price Tag for Listening?

Often I would make the rounds of the chemo lab where patients were taking their infusions. I'd sit down and talk with them, ask how they were doing. I'd joke with them, trying to keep the conversation light. Most of the time they didn't want to talk about their cancer. They'd rather discuss their grandchild's upcoming recital because that was their new goal. It might sound like such a little thing, but to them it was their new goal. It was what they were focusing on and looking forward to.

I have learned the importance of listening. I have learned about the power of the story, so I listen. Often the cancer will come up at some point, but the story will usually center around their relationships, their love, their family. I listen for their unique characteristics, their sense of humor, and their life and struggles. Sometimes those struggles involve the loss of their job or home, and they just need to talk.

In the medical environment, no one else really has the time to sit and listen. The doctor may be in and out quickly, prescribing treatment. The nurses may be rushed, overworked, with ten patients each to care for. The medical assistants whiz in to draw blood, and then they're gone. There is such healing power in the patient's telling their story. Who else is there to listen but a counselor? That's my job. It's what I do.

I would talk to caregivers in the waiting room, listening to their concerns. Sometimes I'd offer practical advice, like serving the patient cold food or using plastic utensils. If the patient had no appetite (common after chemo), I'd recommend protein shakes with ice cream or fruit in them.

I'd tell them that it's okay if the patient's appetite changes from day to day. If she loved baked chicken yesterday but today the thought of it nauseates her, that's not unusual. I remember living on banana Popsicles and grape juice, and I share that with these caregivers.

In the end, sometimes it's the most simple, basic counseling that is the most indispensable. It's nothing more than letting them know someone cares. How do you put a price tag on that?

Oncology counseling first surfaced in the 1980s. When I worked at Morton Plant Hospital in Clearwater, Florida, back in the early 90s, it was still a relatively unique program. We had five full-time counselors whose salaries were paid through a foundation. Unfortunately, with the current health care crisis, most hospitals cannot afford to offer counseling services.

Even now, recent news reports downplaying the importance of self breast exams or postponing regular mammogram screenings until fifty years of age are ridiculous. I was appalled to hear the reports and convinced that it's all about money.

Of course you should do regular self-exams! It doesn't cost a dime! Stupidest thing I've ever heard. I think it's the wrong message no matter where we end up in the medical care debate. Oncologists and OBG-YNs have to set the standards for what works, not the politicians. The phenomenon we continue to see in our offices is that younger and younger women are getting cancer.

Sometimes people can be just like those sheep, blindly following good advice or bad.

Once a Cancer Patient, Always a Cancer Patient

Whenever you go for a regular doctor visit, you're treated as a cancer patient. On the form, you're asked about your medical history, and you check the box beside the word *cancer*. They look at your blood tests and chest x-rays differently. You'll always be checked at a higher level. And that's good! They're looking out for you.

But it can also be bad because you're forever labeled *cancer*. Even after you're considered "cancer free," it's a curse that lives on with you. If you've had lymph nodes removed, you're forever worried about cuts. Something as simple as the prick of a thorn on a rose could cause your arm to swell up twice its size with lymphedema, for which there is no cure. No fluid retention pill or diuretic can help.

The first time I got a cut on my left hand, I cried. When Dick came home, I showed him my cut, the tears still streaming down my face. He kissed it and passed it off.

"No! You don't understand!" I cried. "I could get lymphedema from this little cut!"

He still didn't get it. "Well, now, let's not worry about the small things."

"Dick! Do you not know what lymphedema is? That's when an infection causes the arm to swell up big and fat, and it stays that way forever!"

"Well, you're not going to get that too!"

He was in utter disbelief that there was something else to worry about.

But for cancer patients, there will always be something else to worry about. And the only way to survive is to learn to cope, or you go crazy.

"Sarah" lives on disability. Her husband divorced her the day she was diagnosed with cancer (although he didn't know it at the time). With an "Eeyore" kind of personality, Sarah has fought depression most of her life. Now in her forties, after surviving cancer, she lies around in bed all day, hardly doing anything. At one time she attended church and even took dancing lessons, but she has since stopped both. I tried to convince her to get a job or do some volunteer work just to get out of the house. I explained how therapeutic it can be to take your mind off yourself by helping others.

But Sarah was not open to any of my suggestions. I would estimate somewhere in the vicinity of 30 to 40 percent of my patients were like Sarah, unwilling to take any kind of advice or make any effort to change. People get into patterns in their lives, and they don't want to change. They like where they are.

One of the secretaries in my office once commented on Sarah's situation. "I think she likes to feel this way." And I think there's a lot of truth to that. Patients like Sarah get some sort of reward for acting out this way or feeling this way, no matter how bad it may seem. It becomes a repetitive cycle, earning some kind of reward, even if it comes in the form of pity. In some strange way, they really do like this pattern of behavior. They're comfortable with it. *I can't help it. It's just the way I am.*

At that point, as a counselor, I had to back away. I could not own the frustration. Ultimately the patients have to accept responsibility for themselves. Eventually I had to phase out Sarah's visits as I was unable to help her. I've never been a tough counselor who regularly kicks out patients, primarily because the people I counsel are cancer patients and their families and caregivers. But there comes a time when you realize that there's only so much advice you can give to anyone. If they refuse to be helped, your time is better spent with others.

The "Obstacle" of Cancer

Part of my own personal fear resulted because I saw so many of my patients die. That's the nature of cancer. The patients I see most regularly, week after week after week, are those who are most ill and most likely not to survive. Cancer still has a high mortality rate; certain cancers have higher rates than others. Pancreatic patients are lucky to live six months to a year. Stage IV cancers don't often survive.

I have Stage IIIA cancer. That's not good, and I know it. I've seen too many charts. I've watched too many patients die. I've seen too much . . . *too much.* When I start to feel bad, I'm genuinely afraid I'm going to die.

Yes, the earlier the stage of cancer, the better your prognosis. I still have an 80 percent chance of nonrecurrence. But that 20 percent looms always before me, and that's scary. Yes, we're all going to die eventually. Our grandparents die. Maybe a parent has died. A neighbor dies. The family pet dies. Death is part of life. But that knowledge is small comfort when you have cancer.

I've often used a visual demonstration to describe how death looms ever present in the mind of cancer patients. I place my hand just an inch or two in front of my face, my fingers spread. Whether I turn my head one way or the other, I keep my hand right in front of my face. It blocks my vision of everything else. It is ever before me, interfering with everything I do. It obliterates everything. It is the filter through which I must now view everything in my life.

Older patients handle the presence of this obstacle much better. "I'm eighty-two!" they tell me, as if that explains everything, and in a way it does. It tells me they feel that they've lived a good life and they're aware their days are numbered. But for someone who is thirty-two or forty-five or fifty-two, the obstacle is much more difficult to accept. "What? I have my whole life in front of me! I don't want to die!"

The greatest thrill to me as a counselor is when a patient leaving my office turns to look at me and thanks me for helping.

"Thank you for listening."

"Thank you for helping me feel normal again."

"Thank you for making me see I'm not losing my mind!"

"For one hour, I've felt good. Thank you for that."

As time wore on and they got well, they'd come to see me less and less. They didn't need me anymore.

And that was a good thing.

Chapter 16

CLIMBING THE HIGHEST MOUNTAIN

—*Dick*

I have always loved mountain climbing. Deb thinks I'm crazy. I find joy hanging onto a small sliver of rock with the tip of my fingers three hundred or more feet above the ground. Is that crazy? Free-climbing El Capitan in Yosemite—now, that's crazy! Scooting up steep glaciers and carefully tiptoeing over snow bridges between crevasses whose depth is defined by blues and blacks is a thrill to me. I want to find out what's on top. I want to see the view.

Some call it a death wish. I call it fun.

I also love caving or spelunking. Now, hardcore cavers don't use the word spelunking. Only novices use that term. I've been in places so tight I have to wiggle like a snake just to go a few feet forward. Places with names like the Pancake Room wedge my body between wet ceilings and floors like a vice. Places where I haven't been able to go forward or backward for a while. It's frightening but fun if you don't stay that way for the next ten years.

Even at fifty-seven years old, every time I see a hole in the ground, I want to go in it. Many times I do! I suppose it goes back to my childhood days when my parents couldn't keep me out of storm drains.

No, I haven't climbed Mt. Everest, nor am I the one who discovered Mammoth Cave. My playgrounds include lesser challenges like Mount Rainier, Mount Hood, the Grand Tetons, peaks in Canada and Colorado, and caves in Alabama, Tennessee, and Kentucky. I dream of climbing Mount McKinley in Alaska and hiking to the base camp of Everest. We all have our bucket lists. This is mine. But the bucket is getting holes in it, and some of the items on the list seep out the older I get.

I started enjoying these kinds of activities when I was a child. Dad took me camping numerous times. I could always find a small rock face or boulder to play on. Dad would yell, "Get down from there right now! Do you want to die?"

"Nope."

I've learned some incredible life lessons from these experiences. Maybe not at the time, usually later when I reflect upon them. Like how to deal with fear, pain, weariness, the importance of preparation, teamwork, having faith in yourself, knowing when to stop, knowing when to keep going, dealing with what you can't control, facing danger, experiencing defeat and victory.

My son had this statement inscribed inside his West Point ring: *The view is worth the climb*. For me, it is.

But of all the mountains I have ever climbed or caves I have squeezed into, nothing is more difficult and challenging than cancer. To me, Deb is the highest climber and deepest caver. Everything I have done or ever will do pales in comparison.

When she was diagnosed with cancer, it seemed as if my life stopped. It felt like I was having some metaphysical, out-of-body experience. I was looking down upon someone else, not Deb. This could not be her! But too quickly the harsh reality set in.

Deb stared into a deep hole. She stood at the entrance of a dark cavern whose depth and length was yet unknown. She wasn't a caver. She was frightened at what lay ahead.

Often the rocks surrounding the entrance of a cave are wet and slick. Quite dangerous if the cave drops straight down. As an oncology counselor, Deb knew the depth and danger of cancer. She had watched hundreds of people fall to their death. To her, cancer was like a dark, gaping hole that dropped into a dark abyss, where light disappears quickly, only to be replaced by the darkest dark you will ever "see."

Fear gripped her as she faced the entrance.

There's a point inside a cave where light from the entrance ends and total darkness begins. The effect is ghostly. Eyes are not yet adjusted, and it's very difficult to see where you're going. Your headlamp is on, but you still cannot see well. But as your eyes adjust to the dark, the light becomes more effective. Without it, you cannot keep going.

The diagnosis of cancer quickly casts you into the same kind of darkness. At some point, the light of the past disappears, and light from the entrance is gone. Only the darkness of uncertainty lies ahead. Deb has been there and done that. She has reached up and turned on her light, though it appeared very dim.

Deb is amazing. I don't think she realizes how brave she is.

Inside a cave, dozens of passages can go in different directions. Which do you take—this one or that one? Does that one go anywhere, or does it end after a few feet? Sometimes you simply cannot tell from a distance. All you see is a black hole or opening. You must get down and dirty to find out.

When Deb met with her oncologist, he reviewed various treatment options for her. He discussed the benefits of this one over that one based on the kind of cancer she had. She reviewed them and decided to have neoadjuvant chemotherapy, followed by some sort of surgery, then radiation. It was time to get down and dirty, to see where treatment options might go.

Mud, water, slick rocks, holes, and tight places usually greet you around every corner and turn in a cave. It can be dangerous. You may slip and fall. Once while I was in college, a friend of mine broke his ankle by slipping on loose rock. Thank God we were not too deep inside the cave. A cardinal rule of cavers: Never cave alone, and take at least three light sources. It took four of us to get him out.

Deb has had an impact on hundreds of men, women, and children who have battled cancer. She walked with them each step of the way, listening, guiding, and helping them as they stumbled on their journeys. They all loved her. They love her still.

When she faced some of her darkest times, many of these people called or came by to see her. They brought meals, sent cards, and sat with her during her chemotherapy treatments. They helped her to walk when she was hurting and kept encouraging her to keep the light on. "Never let your light die. Don't turn it off. And if it dies, we'll shine our lights for you."

When you are tired and wet, it's time to turn around and find your way back. But you may not remember which way is up or down or out. It's very frightening to be lost in a cave—and surprisingly easy to do. I've spent hours crawling, climbing, slipping, and falling, trying to find the entrance.

Just when you think you'll stay in there forever, you may shine your light on the cave wall and see an arrow scratched or painted there by another caver. You hope that it shows the direction out. Such markings really tick off most cavers, including me, due to the cosmetic damage it causes. But it can be a godsend to a lost caver. Follow it, and you might find a way out.

Chemotherapy is horrible. Deb got so sick during treatment that some days she didn't want to move a muscle. Nausea, relentless fatigue, and constant pain became her closest companions. But at least there was a scratch on the wall. If she followed the treatment option, maybe she could find her way out. She knew hundreds of other patients who had been there before her. Did they leave a scratch? Did they get out?

At some point, the faint light coming in from the entrance appears. You're excited to see it and know that in just a few minutes, you'll be out. You're muddy and wet, but you're out. And you've been somewhere and seen things most people will never see.

Deb and I were excited as she neared the completion of the Red Devil, a horrible concoction of Adriamycin and Cytoxan, two extremely powerful drugs we hoped would be effective in reducing the extent of her cancer. A regimen of Taxol would follow.

Somewhere in the middle of the chemotherapy, she had an appointment with the surgeon. The examination and sonogram gave us good news. According to the images, the physician's assistant told us, the tumor could barely be seen.

Praise God! Amen! Deb would have a lumpectomy. A mastectomy would not be necessary. She was out of the cave! Muddy, of course, but out!

But an even greater challenged faced her.

As you drive up the road to Paradise (a lodge at 7,000 feet, not the heavenly one) in Mt. Rainier National Park, the view of the mountain inspires a tremendous sense of awe. So big and so beautiful. Snowfields, glaciers, rocks, meadows, wildflowers, cascading waterfalls, refreshing streams, and deep blue skies dance in your eyes. You can't wait to climb that majestic mountain!

Finally out of the cave, Deb now stood at the base of a mountain. Still a little dirty and wet perhaps, but she was drying out. Her mountain was huge. But the good news from her last sonogram gave her courage and hope. Everything was working—the tumors were shrinking, and she was feeling a little better. She stared up at the mountain before her. It was steep, but she felt she could climb it! It began to look beautiful.

When you're climbing up the Muir Snowfield on Rainier, you get extremely tired after several hours. The fifty-pound pack you're carrying gets heavier and heavier. Your breath becomes more labored, and your legs ache. For the first time, it's not fun. In fact, you're ready to set up a climber's yard sale, get rid of all your equipment, and go back down to Paradise. You tell yourself, "This is too steep. I can't do it. I'm not in shape. It ain't worth it. I'm too old!"

The news came totally unexpected.

Another trip to the surgeon revealed that the tumor (or tumors) was a little larger than previously thought. We also found out the cancer was in four lymph nodes, not just two. Apparently we missed getting that information after Deb's lymphadenectomy several weeks earlier. The surgeon seemed less sure about doing the lumpectomy, but still encouraged Deb to try that first. She would always have the option of a mastectomy later.

The burden of cancer became heavier. The mountain she had begun to climb was no longer beautiful. And it wasn't even remotely fun. Deb began to say, "This is too steep. I can't do it. I am not in shape. It ain't worth it."

The lumpectomy took an hour or so. I heard my name called as I sat in the surgical waiting room. Someone told me to go to the small counseling room to meet with the surgeon. I was a nervous wreck when she entered. I was hoping beyond hope she'd gotten all the cancer.

"We found the cancer to be more extensive than we thought."

How I hated that sentence. I despised every noun and verb. Every syllable made me sick. My heart sank, and I began to cry. There was still cancer in there. She was unable to get "clear margins."

The lumpectomy option didn't work. How would I tell Deb?

I have slipped many times on snowfields and glaciers. Most of the time it is nothing more than a couple of feet, something like a brief ice skate. Other times have been longer, more serious and much more dangerous.

While climbing on a steep corridor called the Old Chute on Mount Hood, my crampons (spikes attached to the bottom of my boots) slipped out of some soft snow, and I began to slide on my back and butt.

I was shocked by how quickly it happened and how fast I was sliding. At the bottom a gaping hole called the Devil's Kitchen belched out sulfurous fumes. (Did I mention Mount Hood is a volcano?) Boulders and rocks were stacked like concrete blocks just to the right of that cavernous hole. It looked like I was going into the Kitchen, and I was not hungry!

When climbing on snowfields and glaciers, you use an ice axe. It looks like a small pick. It's used for balance and protection. When you slip and start to slide, you roll over onto your stomach and drive the head of the axe into the snow. Hopefully that will stop you. The procedure is called a self-arrest. And this is what kept me out of that Kitchen.

Upon hearing that the cancer was more extensive than first thought, Deb was devastated. After all the chemo treatments, the cancer had grown even more extensive. Literally, her left breast was eaten up with the disease. Some was still in her. I can't imagine hearing that—*still in her*. She had fallen, sliding down toward a gaping hole, headed for the rocks, too weak to self-arrest. Frankly, she didn't care if she stopped at all.

When we set up base camp on Ingraham Glacier on Rainier, we practiced crevasse rescue procedures. We found shallow crevasses and set up anchors and pulleys to make sure that if someone fell in, we could arrest their fall and get them out. So I decided to be the rescue dummy. I fell in and shouted, "Falling!" For a few seconds I was terrified. When the rope stopped me, it felt great. "I've got ya!" my buddy shouted. They set up the pulleys and got me out.

With the news of the lumpectomy, Deb began to fall. She was tired of climbing. Maybe she just let go. I couldn't blame her. I certainly would have. But I was not going to let her fall too far. I had the rope. In fact, many people held the rope along with me. My sisters, her sisters, nephews, nieces, brothers-in-law, friends, and hundreds of former patients had their hands on it along with me. She was on belay whether she liked it or not. For a long time she just hung there.

"We've got you, Deb! We won't let you fall any farther. You can do it! Start climbing again!"

It took a while, but she moved.

Deb hung up the phone after talking to her oncologist. On an MRI some white dots appeared sprinkled through the right breast. Deb immediately decided to have a double mastectomy.

At about 12,000 feet on Mt. Rainier is a steep rocky climb called Disappointment Cleaver. It is the crux of the route. Get beyond it, and the most difficult and technical part of the climb is over. This does not mean there are no more dangerous crevasses or that the slopes are less steep. But get to the top of it, and you either feel confident you'll make it the rest of the way or you'll quit. I guess that's why it's called Disappointment Cleaver.

The mastectomy took about two-and-a-half hours. Back again in the surgical waiting room, I heard my name called. I went to the counseling room where I met the surgeon. "Everything went fine, and she lost very little blood." She would be in recovery for an hour or so, then I could see her.

Once they allowed me to see her, I felt so sad for her. Deb would not let go of my hand. She begged me not to leave her. I'm sure it was part emotion, but also part medication. (I told the nurses I'd like some of that to take back home with me!) But the worst part was now behind her. Deb had survived the Cleaver.

When I neared the summit of Rainier, I was exhausted. I had been climbing since 12:30 that morning, and it was almost 8 a.m. How much farther? A team on its way down passed us as we laboriously climbed. I asked one of them how far it was to the top. He told me the sweetest news I'd ever heard: "You are so close to the top you could piss on it!"

And in a few minutes, we made it. *Wow.* What a view!

When a fellow climber is tired and wonders if he can keep going up, sometimes a stronger climber will "short-rope" him. But the stronger climber will only do this if he feels that the weary climber can make it both up and back down. Climbers are generally roped together about thirty-five to forty feet apart. To short-rope, the length of rope between the two climbers is obviously shortened. The stronger climber can assist the weaker one by pulling him. His strength becomes part of the weaker climber's strength.

Most of the time, short-roping is used on the way down. The effect is reversed. The stronger climber assists the weaker one to make it down safely.

The pain and fatigue exhausted Deb after her mastectomy. I kept on encouraging her that the worst was over. "You've almost made it. You can see the top from here. You are so close, you can (okay, I won't use that word again)—*urinate* on it!"

Family, friends, patients, and doctors got out the short rope. The double mastectomy was done. We pulled, and she held on tight. She was so exhausted, but then it was over. We cried as she finally stepped onto the summit of her treatment.

She made it! And oh, what a view!

There may still be caves and mountains ahead. We hope not. If there are, we will do whatever it takes to make it out and up. Deb can do it. She has done it before. She is the greatest spelunker—I mean caver—and strongest climber I will ever know.

Chapter 17

BEGINNING

—Dick and Deb

After finishing all the chapters in our original book outline, we felt that something was missing. We had talked about many aspects of cancer and how they have affected us. In most cases, these aspects could and should be seen as very negative. We talked about tears, pain, struggles, money problems, horrible medicines, surgeries, fear, panic, death, anxiety, and so much more. So we decided to finish our book with something more positive. Not an easy task with a subject like cancer.

The last chapter in many books is titled "Conclusion" or "Epilogue." We decided we don't like either one of these words. We especially don't care for conclusion. Epilogue sounds more official, even stately and regal. But it is a conclusion as well. We hate that one too.

When it comes to dealing with cancer, there really is no conclusion or epilogue. It still continues. Whether a person is healed or not, cancer never goes away. If there's no recurrence of the disease after five years, many patients are considered to be healed. But the memory of cancer still lives in every bone and fiber of the body.

The title "Cancer Survivor" stays forever stamped on the forehead. The words blink like dirty red neon signs advertising sleazy bars where cancer goes out for drinks to meet women. There is always the fear that it will come back. Sometimes it doesn't. Many times it does.

Also, should a loved one die of cancer, there is never a "conclusion" either. Forever, cancer will be the one to blame. Husbands, wives, children, sisters, brothers, and everyone who knew the person dying of it will remember the C-word. "Oh, my wife died of cancer last year."

Or "My mother had brain cancer twenty years ago and died at home." On and on it goes like a broken record.

But sometimes, the word is used in a much better context. "Praise the Lord, my cancer has gone away!" Or "The surgeon got all of the cancer!" Or "I used to have cancer." We like these. But still cancer remains the focal point as though it's not really gone, just away on an extended vacation only to return well-rested and ready to get back to work.

Conclusion and epilogue are so morbid anyway. Who wants to end a book about cancer with that? It seems so final. Might as well just say "The End."

Since we refuse to use either of these words, we needed to come up with a new one. After discussing the matter, we decided to call this final chapter "Beginning." Our life is just beginning. We must see every day as a beginning. It is fresh. It is new. It is filled with hope. There is no end in sight. And the best days are just beginning!

Cancer has taught us so many things. Many are bad, but some are good. When we lived in Florida, horrible thunderstorms often rolled in during the late evening hours. Dangerous flashes of lightning and torrential rain reminded us of the awesome power of nature. But just as soon as the storm began, it passed, leaving a renewed freshness in the air. For just a few moments it actually felt cool outside. That is unusual in sunny Florida.

Cancer is like those thunderstorms—one after another. But just when you think it will never stop raining, the skies clear and the evening seems fresh and renewed. We cherish those moments. Yes, cancer has been mostly negative, but there are some good lessons we have learned while riding out the storm.

We have learned to celebrate the "good" days.

—*Dick*

Deb called me from her office. Usually when she calls, she mentions how tired she is and how tight and uncomfortable her chest feels. But this time, she had a lift in her voice. She sounded normal, even happy. She has always been the positive one in our family; however, since she has had cancer, this positive dynamic has rarely surfaced. But on this call she sounded so cheerful.

She had received a good report from her blood tests. "Dick, it's the first time I don't feel like I'm going to die of cancer." We decided to celebrate and went out to dinner. She looked beautiful, confident, and relieved. It was a great night.

—Deb

But just the next day, I had a voicemail on my phone from the oncologist's office telling me that one of my blood tests showed a higher-than-normal calcium level in my bloodstream. High levels of calcium could be associated with cancer spreading to my bones.

The good day I celebrated the day before was now only a memory. Cancer repeatedly takes you by surprise. Just when you think everything looks great, something else shows up to kill your confidence. So you need to cherish and celebrate each good day because the next day may bring different news.

We have learned not to sweat the small stuff.

—Deb

Life is so short, with or without cancer. Most people spend too much time worrying about things that will never happen. It is so easy to get into this way of thinking. Small, insignificant things can be blown way out of proportion.

Last week I was so frustrated at my computer because I couldn't find a document I had saved. Ranting and raving, I called Dick at work. "I can't find this stupid letter on this stupid computer! And the check requisition is lost, and my boss is going to be mad at me!" Before he could even answer me, I cried, "And I don't know how to change the ring tone on my phone. Someone told me I still had a Christmas song on it."

He said he was sorry, and then he laughed so hard. I paused and thought about what I had just said. How important was it at that particular moment to change my ring tone? This was not a life and death situation. Finally I laughed too.

—Dick

One thing I hate is getting up in the morning and walking down the hallway to the stairs. It's right there, strategically centered in the very middle of the carpet. In plain sight. Deliberately positioned there to be stepped in by an unsuspecting passerby. It's brown, in a small pile, and it smells.

The anger swells up in me. How can a five-pound Chihuahua leave ten pounds of dog poop on the floor? I get loud and march down the hallway like a soldier ready for battle, mumbling words ministers should not say. I want Deb to hear me. I want to wake her up. In a loud voice, I say, "Debbie, your stupid dog messed on the floor again." Then I rush the bed, looking for the tiny, evil perpetrator. "Where is that stupid little animal?"

At this point, Deb is anxious, mad, and hates me. She protects Belle like a Kodiak mama bear protects her cubs. What a great way to begin a new day.

So what? The dog messed on the floor. It's not one of the biblical signs of the coming of the Antichrist. Why should I let it ruin Deb's day and mine? It's nothing a little toilet paper and Resolve can't take care of. Cancer leaves enough mess for us to worry about.

We have learned to trust God more.
—*Dick*

I always like to be in control. Not because I'm a control freak. It's because I am a very anxious and nervous person. I try to avoid my anxiousness as much as possible.

For instance, each night before I go to bed, I have everything ready for the next day. I have every stitch of clothing I will need from shirt to pants hanging or lying right within reach. Soap, towel, socks, shoes, toothbrush, toothpaste, razor, shaving cream, underwear—you name it—are all within arm's length. I can get ready in a coma. I want the morning to go as smoothly as possible, with no surprises. Having no clean socks can send me into a maniacal frenzy. You don't want to be here if that happens.

I get up at 5:15 a.m. so I can be on the way to work by 5:30. Yes, I can get ready in fifteen minutes. I get up this early so I can avoid the anxiety triggered by Atlanta traffic.

With Deb's cancer, I cannot be in control. There is nothing I can do to prepare for what may happen on a particular day. I can't fix it or make it go away. So I stay anxious most of the time.

I'm a minister, so you would think the first thing I'd do is pray. Strange as it may sound, sometimes that's the last thing I do. I think I'm strong enough to deal with it on my own. But guess what? I can't. The burden is too great. The only way I can try to relieve this is to recognize I need help to carry the load. I have to try to give it to God.

First Peter 5:7 says, "Cast all your anxiety on him because he cares for you." When I read this, I'm reminded that the very nature of the God I have tried to represent is one of love, mercy, and compassion. Even though I might not understand all the reasons why cancer has stricken Deb, I have to believe He cares for me too and will help me to carry the burden.

—Deb

I am a very trusting person. I've been that way all my life. Some people have said that it's because I'm very naïve. Dick would agree. Someone could be standing in front of me holding a knife, and I would think they're looking for the Thanksgiving turkey to carve.

But when it comes to my faith, I am not naïve. I know there is a God who watches over me. He held my hand when I was lying alone in my bed so sick from the chemo I couldn't raise my head off the pillow. He gently wiped my tears when I thought only Belle was there to watch me cry. He lifted me up when I could not lift myself. He listened while I prayed and always responded in His quiet stillness, relaxing and loving me.

I now know more than ever that Jesus will never leave or forsake me, just as He promised. Dick told you about the time I almost died after Mary was born. I saw Jesus, and He told me not to worry, that everything would be okay. I believed that from the bottom of my heart then, and today I still believe it.

I still have moments of great pain and fear. I panic and become anxious. I pray and ask for peace. Philippians 4:6-7 says: "Do not be anxious about anything, but in everything, by prayer and petition, with thanksgiving, present your requests to God. And the peace of God, which transcends all understanding, will guard your hearts and your minds in Christ Jesus."

At times I may wonder where God is in all this. I may feel all alone and forsaken. I may fear I am going to die. But I have come to a renewed trust in what Paul wrote in Romans 8:38-39: "For I am convinced that neither death nor life, neither angels nor demons, neither the present nor the future, nor any powers, neither height nor depth, nor anything else in all creation, will be able to separate us from the love of God that is in Christ Jesus our Lord."

And that includes cancer.

We have learned that it's okay to cry.
—Dick

By now you know I am a very sentimental person. It's not difficult for me to "tune up and bawl." My granny often used that expression. I cry out of happiness, regret, bad memories, fond memories, and pain. You name it, I've cried about it. I am sure you have as well. But I usually do this in private when no one else is around. I do my best to hide my tears. I will leave the room, go outside to wipe my tears, or get in the car. I think crying makes me look very weak. Most men don't want to be weak. Men are supposed to be strong and virile. Crying is for babies. If this is true, then change my diaper.

Crying is almost a daily part of my routine. Usually it happens on my way to work in the early morning. I have an hour commute, so I have plenty of time. I think about Deb and all the pain she is going through, among a thousand other thoughts about her cancer. I have learned that I need to cry. And it's strange, sometimes Deb needs to see me cry too. It's not for pity. I think it's a recognition that we're in this together.

Crying becomes a language of love. It communicates nonverbally how much I need her and she needs me. During those times we just hold each other as I wipe her tears and she wipes mine.

—Deb

As a counselor, I hear many sob stories. Dick always remarks about my ability to leave all these stories at work. When I come home, I am home and don't bring the office with me. He's amazed.

I remember a specific instance when I couldn't.

Years ago at Morton Plant Hospital in Clearwater, Florida, I was counseling a beautiful thirty-three-year-old wife and mother in my office. She had been diagnosed with C.L.L. (Chronic Lymphocytic Leukemia). She told me she was so scared of dying. I assured her that her type of cancer was very manageable and encouraged her not to worry.

The next day when I entered the hospital, I found out she was in a coma caused by a massive brain hemorrhage. I rushed to her room. Her husband had been told his wife was dying. Their little boy was in the room playing with a toy truck. "Look at my red truck!" he said. "It goes zoom zoom!" Then he asked a couple of questions that broke my heart. "Is my mommy sick?" I told him, "Yes, she is very sick." "Is my mommy going to die?" His dad began to cry as he told his son the truth. The little boy ran to his mother's bed, took her hand and cried, "Mommy, Mommy, please don't leave me! Please don't!" I had to leave the room, and I cried my eyes out.

This story came home with me and stayed for many days.

I remember when I first called Dick when he was in Dallas, right after my appointment with my gynecologist. My voice was shaking, and tears streamed down my face.

Dick usually tries to console me whenever I start to cry. He attempts to control the situation. He hates to see me this way. He tells me that everything will be okay. But sometimes that makes me angry. I want to cry. I *need* to cry. I need to think it will not be okay. So I tell him, "Dick, just shut up and let me cry."

Over the months, he has learned. I don't have to tell him to shut up anymore. No words need to be spoken. He lets my tears say it all.

We have learned to never stop climbing.
—*Deb*

I tell Dick all the time, "No, you are not going climbing. That mountain is dangerous. It is icy this time of year. You are too old." He tries to tell me that Longs Peak in Colorado is not that hard in the winter, and he will be fine. "Give me a break! I can do it!" he says. I then conclude that he is stupid and too old. Usually he goes anyway with a promise that he'll be safe and make wise decisions. So far he has. I have to let him go.

I have climbed a mountain too. It was dangerous too.

The mountain to recovery was high, almost too high for me to climb. The chemotherapy, surgery, radiation, and hundreds of other difficulties made me so weak that even the thought of climbing was inconceivable. Most of the time I was much too tired to even think about it. Honestly, I just didn't want to. But so many people were depending on me and supporting me that I couldn't give up.

With the encouragement of Dick and many others, I took one step at a time. I slipped and fell so often. I got up, only to fall again and again. Each time I got up, the summit looked closer. That gave me hope.

With each passing day I got higher and higher, stronger and stronger. And soon I could see the top. I gathered all the strength I could muster and took one more step.

Dick was right. What a view! I was on top and thrilled it was over! But I pray I will never have to climb another one.

—*Dick*

When Scott and I climbed Mount Athabasca in Canada a few years ago, I thought it would be a piece of cake. Frankly, as mountains go, it was not that high, only a little over 11,000 feet. But as we started our ascent, it seemed like Mount Everest. It was steep. We climbed up to the left of the glacier head wall and finally onto the glacier itself. We began to make the long trek up. As we climbed, we became totally exhausted. The summit seemed impossibly far away.

Whenever I'm tired of climbing, I always pick a point somewhere ahead and make it my goal to get there. It may be a rock outcrop or something else. The summit seems too far away. But I know if I make it from one small goal to another, eventually I might make it to the top.

Deb moved from one small goal to another. Her first major goal was making it through the chemotherapy. Even though she felt it was impossible, she took eight treatments one by one to finish.

My heart broke for her. After each treatment the effects began to surface. Nausea, weakness, rashes, and pain welcomed her around every corner. I began to see her beautiful blonde hair thin out strand by strand until there was no more to thin. She felt so ugly. But her first goal was to get through the eighth treatment, and she did.

Her second goal was to make it through surgeries. Unfortunately it took her twice as long to do this. Two surgeries were needed, a lumpectomy, and then a double mastectomy. But she made it through. The last goal was to finish her radiation. She took one treatment at a time, and soon it was over.

We had such a celebration when her cancer treatments stopped. Cards, flowers, and smiley-face balloons filled our kitchen. We hung banners on the walls, and the phone rang constantly, bringing congratulations from family and friends.

Honestly, I don't think Deb realizes what she has done. I am not sure she understands how incredibly brave and strong she is. She faced a mountain none of us would like to climb. Yes, she had encouragement, prayers, and help from hundreds of people, and she is so appreciative of that. She knows how much that helped her to make it through.

But that's only part of the reason.

As Scott and I neared the summit of Mount Athabasca, we were both physically exhausted. Scott encouraged me, and I encouraged him. But make no mistake. If I was going to make it to the summit, I had to do it. No one else could do it for me, not even Scott.

Deb did it, and no one else could do it for her.

Yes, Deb may appear dainty, feminine, a typical blonde, sweet, innocent, and mild mannered. That's just a smoke screen. Trust me. I have lived with her for thirty years, and I know her. When she has to be, she is a fingernail-clawing, hard-biting, tough-talking, fist-punching, boot-kicking, butt-whooping babe who can look death right in the face and growl, "Go ahead, make my day."

We could continue and list so many more things that we have learned: patience, courage, teamwork, trust, thankfulness, and more. But by far, the greatest thing is:

We have learned to love more deeply.
—Dick and Deb

In I Corinthians 13:4-7, Paul said: "Love is patient, love is kind. It does not envy, it does not boast, it is not proud. It is not rude, it is not self-seeking, it is not easily angered, it keeps no record of wrongs. Love does not delight in evil but rejoices with the truth. It always protects, always trusts, always hopes, always perseveres."

On December 30, 1978, two young and scared people began a long journey of life together. Hands clasped, they looked into each others eyes and made a commitment to be husband and wife before God and man. They promised it would be for better or for worse, for richer or for poorer, in sickness and in health, for as long as they both shall live.

When all the dust settles and every attempt has been made to determine the effect this disease has had on us, one thing stands out: the undeniable, unquestionable, never-ending discovery and reaffirmation that we are desperately in love with each other.

No matter what happens, cancer will never take that away.

ACKNOWLEDGMENTS

From Dick

To my brothers-in-law Don and David—thank you for not only loving my sisters but me too. You have spent so many nights alone when my sisters Sharon and Pat rushed to be by our side. Words cannot express how much my sisters mean to Deb and me. Sharon and Pat, you have truly been there for us and have helped us out financially, emotionally, and spiritually.

To my nephew Justin and his beautiful wife Kirsten, you have done so much for us and made many trips to fix up our home. Shane and Shannon, we appreciate your prayers.

I am so thankful to all the cancer survivors, past and present, who touched Deb's heart and gave her the inspiration to become the greatest oncology counselor in the universe!

My son, Scott, you are Daddy's best buddy. And my beautiful daughter, Mary, you are Daddy's little girl. You have always believed that your daddy could do everything—even write a book!

From Deb

My "YaYa" Sisters have supported us with their prayers, support, laughter, and tears!

The staff at Northwest Georgia Oncology Centers, especially Dr. Frank McCoy, Jan West, and Cyndy Martin, thank you for your tremendous medical care and friendship. You are more than employees; you are my family!

Sydney Alter and Suzanne Johnson-Berns, thank you for supporting me when I first mentioned this book and making me believe I could do it.

My children, Scott and Mary—you are my reason for striving and living each day with challenge and hope. Thank you both for calling me every day, no matter if you were in the middle of a desert or an exam. I love you more than you will ever know.

A special blessing and word of thanks to all my patients, who are truly survivors in every sense of the word. You each have taught me so much over the past eighteen years. Thank you for your inspiration.

From Both of Us

Diane Moody has laughed and cried with us. You are the very definition of a true friend. You were the first to believe in our story and helped us to write it. Thank you from the bottom of our hearts.

Joy DeKok and Joan Shoup at Sheaf House Publishers, you have given us an incredible opportunity to share our hearts with thousands affected by cancer. We will forever be grateful.

ENDNOTES

Chapter 2

[1]Gynecology. Dictionary.com. *Online Etymology Dictionary*. Douglas Harper, Historian. http://dictionary.reference.com/browse/gynecology (accessed: September 2, 2009).

Chapter 4

[1]Reverend. *Online Etymology Dictionary*. Douglas Harper, Historian. http://dictionary.reference.com/browse/reverend (accessed: October 20, 2009).

[2]Reverend. Dictionary.com. *Dictionary.com Unabridged*. Random House, Inc. http://dictionary.reference.com/browse/Reverend (accessed: October 20, 2009).

[3]Reverence. Dictionary.com. *Dictionary.com Unabridged*. Random House, Inc. http://dictionary.reference.com/browse/Reverence (accessed: October 20, 2009).

Chapter 5

[1]Elisabeth Kübler-Ross, M.D., The Stages of Grief, *On Death and Dying*, (New York: Scribner, 1969) with permission from the Elisabeth Kübler-Ross Foundation, www.ekrfoundation.org

Chapter 8

[1]Mercy. By permission. From *Merriam-Webster's Collegiate® Dictionary*, *11th Edition©2010* by Merriam-Webster, Incorporated (www.Merriam-Webster.com).

[2]Compassion. By permission. From *Merriam-Webster's Collegiate® Dictionary, 11th Edition©2010* by Merriam-Webster, Incorporated (www.Merriam-Webster.com).

[3]Forbearing. By permission. *From Merriam-Webster's Collegiate® Dictionary, 11th Edition©2010* by Merriam-Webster, Incorporated (www.Merriam-Webster.com).

Chapter 9

[1]Kathleen McCue, *How to Help Children Through a Parent's Serious Illness* (New York: St. Martin's Press, © 1994), p. 22

Chapter 11

[1] "Physical Activity and Breast Cancer Risk," Fact Sheet #19, March 2008, The Program on Breast Cancer and Environment Risk Factors in New York State, Julie A. Napieralski, PhD and Carol Devine PhD, RD, Cornell University, http://envirocancer.cornell.edu/factsheet/diet/fs19.exercise.cfm

[2]Ginny Owens and Kyle Matthews, *If You Want Me To*, © 1999 ABOVE THE RIM MUSIC/BMG SONGS, INC./CAREERS-BMG MUSIC PUBLISHING, INC./FINAL FOUR MUSIC. All rights reserved. Used by permission.

Chapter 13

[1]National Cancer Institute, *Annual Report to the Nation Finds Declines in Cancer Incidence and Death Rates; Special Feature Reveals Wide Variations in Lung Cancer Trends across States, 11/25/2008* The findings come from the "Annual Report to the Nation on the Status of Cancer, 1975-2005, Featuring Trends in Lung Cancer, Tobacco Use and Tobacco Control", online Nov. 25, 2008, and appearing in the Dec. 2, 2008, Journal of the National Cancer Institute.
http://www.cancer.gov/newscenter/pressreleases/ReportNation 2008Release

Chapter 15

[1]"Faith, Hope and Healing by *Bernie Siegel, MD*." Bernie Siegel, MD.com. October 12, 2009.
http://www.berniesiegelmd.com/faith_hope_and_healing.htm.